Second Edition

Instructor Edition

Biological Inquiry
A Workbook of Investigative Cases
for

Campbell • Reece

Biology
Eighth Edition

Margaret Waterman
Southeast Missouri State University

Ethel Stanley
BioQUEST Curriculum Consortium and Beloit College

PEARSON

Benjamin
Cummings

San Francisco   Boston   New York
Cape Town   Hong Kong   London   Madrid   Mexico City
Montreal   Munich   Paris   Singapore   Sydney   Tokyo   Toronto

Editor-in-Chief: Beth Wilbur
Senior Editorial Manager: Ginnie Simione Jutson
Senior Supplements Project Editor: Susan Berge
Project Editor: Kim Wimpsett
Managing Editor: Michael Early, Michael Penne
Production Supervisor: Jane Brundage
Photo Researcher: Maureen Spuhler
Photo Editor: Donna Kalal
Manufacturing Buyer: Michael Early
Executive Marketing Manager: Lauren Harp
Production Management and Composition: S4Carlisle, Judy Ludowitz
Cover Designer: Yvo Riezebos Design
Text and Cover Printer: Technical Communications Services

Cover Image: Magnolia Flower–Corbis. Photographer: Chris Fox.

ISBN-13: 978-0-321-49435-1
ISBN-10: 0-321-49435-0

PEARSON

Benjamin
Cummings

www.aw-bc.com
1 2 3 4 5 6 7 8 9 10 – TCS – 10 09 08 07

Preface to the Instructor's Edition

Biological Inquiry: A Workbook of Investigative Cases includes eight cases that are designed to accompany each unit and two cases that are multi-unit for *Biology,* 8th edition, of Campbell and Reece. Investigative cases will provide your students with the opportunity to actively develop an understanding of the science in each case. While participating in the investigative case experience, students will pose questions, analyze data, think critically, examine the relationship between evidence and conclusions, construct hypotheses, investigate options, graph data, interpret results, communicate scientific arguments, and connect to the real world. Each case will actively involve students in the experimental nature of science and give them insight into how we know what we know.

There are multiple approaches to teaching and learning in undergraduate education. Investigative Case–Based Learning (ICBL) is not only recognized as an approach for teaching scientifically (Handelsman, et al., 2005), but also for embracing authentic learning strategies that are transforming higher education (Lombardi, 2007). We developed ICBL, with support from the National Science Foundation, and wrote this case book specifically to address these issues in contemporary undergraduate biology education.

In a major study of undergraduate biology education in the United States, the National Research Council (NRC) reported that while biology research is more interdisciplinary, quantitative, and collaborative than it was in the past, undergraduate biology education is not (National Research Council, 2003). Cech (2003), president of the Howard Hughes Medical Institute (HHMI), argues that the lack of balance between biology research and biology teaching has resulted in "a decreasing percentage, here in the United States, of students who wish to pursue research careers; school districts that struggle to find qualified K–12 science teachers; and a public that has only a hazy understanding of the research advances that are sweeping through our society."

In its 1996 document, Shaping the Future: New Expectations for Undergraduate Education in Science, Mathematics, Engineering and Technology, the National Science Foundation (NSF) advises that practice in making decisions involving science should be part of undergraduate science courses and specifically recommends that science educators "build into every course inquiry ('involving the student in asking questions and finding answers') the processes of science, a knowledge of what practitioners do, and the excitement of cutting edge research" (NSF, 1996, p. 53) as well as "devise and use pedagogy that develops skills for communications, teamwork, critical thinking and lifelong learning in each student" (NSF, 1996, p. iii).

The National Science Foundation further recommends that science educators "start with the student's experience . . . and relate the subject matter to things the student already knows"(NSF, 1996, pp. 65–66). In addition, the NRC (Bransford, 2000) advises that learners come "to formal education with a range of prior knowledge, skills, beliefs and concepts. This affects what learners notice, how they reason and solve problems, and how they remember" (p. 10). The public faces decisions such as voting on an air quality referendum, becoming concerned about the levels of pesticides in drinking water, determining whether or not to donate blood, performing jury duty in which an understanding of forensics data may be critical to the case, or deciding whether or not to vaccinate their own children. The NSF raises the concern that the public may not be able to engage in the critical thinking necessary to make these judgments.

The international Commission on Biology Education (CBE) has raised a similar concern specifically addressing biology education. "Influencing almost all our activities, from inception to the grave, this revolution will require profound decisions with respect to the ethical, legal, social, cultural, educational, and development issues that are sure to arise, affecting our personal lives and society in ways that we have never experienced before" (Vohra, 2000). From a global perspective, a necessary goal of biology education is to "develop citizens' biological literacy, i.e., provide them with the core biological knowledge, the ability to formulate questions, and an idea of how and where to look for answers, in order to help them to participate responsibly in the life of the society" (Younès, 2000).

Investigative Case–Based Learning approaches build on the recognition that most learners seek information when encountering an incident or situation in their lives, such as a medical situation, local environmental controversy, or employment requirement, that generates a strong need-to-know about the science underlying their concern (Bertot and McClure, 2002). Students pose specific questions to investigate scientific problems that they find meaningful within the issues defined by case. They employ a variety of methods and resources, including traditional laboratory and field techniques, software simulations and models, data sets, Internet-based tools, and information retrieval methods. In the process, they also learn to

- locate and manage information,
- develop reasonable answers to the questions,
- use scientific inquiry strategies and methods,
- provide support for their conclusions, and
- work on decision-making abilities.

By providing entry points for women and minority learners (Sellers, Friedrich, Saleem, and Burstyn, 2005; Ramaley and Haggett 2005; Center for the Integration of Research, Teaching, and Learning, CIRTL 2005; Ezeliora, 2002), the use of investigative cases is one strategy for developing an invitational framework for diverse learners to gain a deeper understanding of the biological sciences.

Each set of investigations begins with a scenario (case) in which people are in a situation that requires some understanding of specific biological concepts. The cases are designed to help your students make connections between the content in the textbook and its application to realistic settings outside the classroom. Several different investigations are linked to each case. The decisions or issues in each case arise within contexts to which students can readily relate. Research has shown repeatedly that when science is learned within a meaningful context, retention is significantly increased and the ability to apply this information is enhanced.

How do these investigative cases differ from other case studies or problem-based learning materials? Investigative cases are meant to initiate student inquiry into the science. The primary purpose of many case studies in science and those used in medical schools is to cover material or get students to look up information. Few have scientific investigations linked to them. Ideally, an investigative case would be the starting place for students to conduct open-ended investigations of questions posed by them. In this workbook format, there are brief, well-defined investigations that will relate to some questions the students are likely to raise. Suggestions and resources for more open-ended investigations for each case can be found at http://www. masteringbio.com under the Case Book tab.

One of the most difficult elements of scientific inquiry is learning how to ask good questions. Investigative cases, when coupled with case analysis, provide opportunities for students to raise thoughtful questions that interest them. You may want to use the questions that students raise during the case analysis for open-ended investigations, research papers, or discussion of ethics or science-technology-society issues. You could provide laboratory or field or computational investigations based on the problem space in the case, or you may work with students to develop their own investigations. The questions students raise are powerful tools for engaging them fully in learning. Investigative cases help students identify what they already know and what they need to know. This may set the stage for highly motivated learning in subsequent related lectures and labs.

Instructors from every type of undergraduate institution have expressed their surprise at the ease with which their students raise relevant questions and at the power of cases to engage their students in seeking new information and applying new methodologies.

Student Edition Features

Case: A compelling, one-page scenario that relays the realistic problem under consideration.

Case Analysis Sheet: This form provides an opportunity for students to identify key ideas, what they already know, and what they need to find out.

Core Investigations: Each case includes several investigations that relate directly to the case issues and content in *Biology*.

Critical Reading: This is usually the first core investigation. It requires students to apply information from the related textbook chapter(s) in order to further understand the issues in the case.

Additional Investigations: Investigations that relate to the case but that might extend beyond the most closely related textbook material.

Case Book Website: The Case Book tab on the www.masteringbio.com website will connect students to a Web page for each of the eight cases. There, students will find resources, references, and links needed to complete each case, along with resources for more open-ended investigations.

Instructor's Edition Features

Case Overview: A table describing the goals for each investigation and the inquiry skills students will use. This table will help you select which investigations most appropriately fit your own course goals.

Campbell-Related Resources: A table correlating the case investigations to the textbook and media materials.

Suggested Answers:

- The **case** is displayed with significant terms and phrases in boldface.
- The **completed Case Analysis sheet** will help you lead a case discussion and anticipate the issues and questions your students are likely to raise.

- The **suggested answers for the investigations** will help you to anticipate student responses and can also serve as a guide to grading. We did not assign point values.

Suggestions for Using These Cases and Investigations

Investigative cases lend themselves to many uses in teaching, and they are a flexible tool for science learning. Each case can stand alone. If you are just beginning to use cases, you might try one in the first semester to get your feet wet and work out the kinks. The next semester, you might try more than one. Similarly, each investigation within a case can stand alone so that you can assign just the parts of the case that fit your course and your schedule. If you ask students to do significant work on the case, it is important to evaluate their work even if you choose to give extra credit points. As many of us have observed, busy students rarely give significant effort to assignments that do not affect their grades. The cases and investigations in this book, as well as the open-ended investigations on the website, can be used in many settings, such as lecture hall, lab, or an online bulletin board. They can be assigned for homework, or students can do them to supplement their learning. Students can work individually or in groups (we strongly recommend working in groups during Case Analysis). Instructors have used cases similar to these to

- Introduce a new topic in the course
- Preassess prior knowledge of the class using the case analysis discussion
- Initiate discussion during lecture
- Connect to an extended laboratory investigation
- Ask students to design their own investigations based on the questions they raised in Case Analysis
- Direct students to conduct more open-ended investigations, such as those on the Campbell website at the Case Book tab
- Structure an entire section of a course
- Assess student learning (and ability to pose questions) by including a case and case analysis on an exam
- Set the context for a regular lab session by starting with a case before the lab and returning to it after
- Introduce the need for a specific lab technology or method
- Provide common background for independent research reports
- Address multicultural perspectives
- Integrate historical incidents (e.g., the flu epidemic of 1918)
- Introduce modeling and simulation software
- Assess data interpretation skills
- Introduce experimental design
- Prepare students for a field trip

We hope that investigative cases will become yet another tool in your teaching portfolio. Investigative Case–Based Learning (ICBL) is based on educational research and has been field tested in college classrooms. Additional background information on science learning and ICBL can be found in the following resources:

Bertot, J., and C. McClure. 2002. *Public libraries and the Internet 2002: Internet connectivity and networked services.* Florida State University, Information Use Management & Policy Institute. http://www.ii.fsu.edu/Projects/2002pli/2002.plinternet.study.pdf, last accessed 6 May 2006.

Bransford, J. D., A. L. Brown, and R. R. Cocking (Eds.). 1999. *How people learn: Brain, mind, experience and school.* Washington, DC: National Academy Press. (Available online.)

Board of Life Sciences. 2003. *Bio 2010: Transforming undergraduate education for future research biologists.* Washington, DC: National Academy Press. (Available online.)

Cech T. 2003. Rebalancing teaching and research. *Science,* 299:165.

Center for the Integration of Research, Teaching, and Learning. 2005. Science teaching using cases, http://cirtl.wceruw.org/diversityinstitute/resources/case-book/scienceteachingusingcases.htm, last accessed 6 December 2006.

Ezeliora, Bernadette. 2002. Developing engineering skills in female students by incorporating local practices into science education. http://www.serve.com/awis/ezeliora.html, last accessed October 11, 2007.

Lombardi, Marilyn, M. 2007. Approaches That Work: How Authentic Learning Is Transforming Higher Education. Educause Learning Initiative Paper 5. http://www.educause.edu/ir/library/pdf/ELI3013.pdf. Accessed September 29, 2007.

Handelsman, J., D. Ebert-May, R. Beichner, P. Bruns, A. Chang, R. DeHaan, J. Gentile, S. Lauffer, J. Stewart, S. M. Tilghman, and W. B. Wood. 2004. Scientific teaching. *Science* 304:521–522.

National Research Council. 2003. *BIO2010: Transforming undergraduate education for future research biologists.* Washington, DC: National Academy Press.

National Science Foundation. 1996. *Shaping the future: New expectations for undergraduate education in science, mathematics, engineering, and technology.* Washington, DC: Document NSF 96–139.

National Science Foundation. 2004. *Invention and impact: Building excellence in undergraduate science, technology, engineering, and mathematics (STEM) education.* Washington, DC: Document NSF 9–10.

Peterson, N. S., and J. R. Jungck. 1988. Problem-posing, problem-solving, and persuasion in biology. *Academic Computing,* 2:4–17, 48–50.

Ramaley, J. A., and R. Haggett. 2005. Engaged and engaging science: A component of a good liberal education. *Peer Review* (Winter) 8–12.

Sellers, Sherrill L., Katherine Friedrich, Tabassum Saleem, and Judith N. Burstyn. 2005. Case studies in inclusive teaching in science, technology, engineering and mathematics. Madison, WI: Diversity Institute of the Center for the Integration of Research, Teaching, and Learning (CIRTL). http://cirtl.wceruw.org/diversityinstitute/resources/case-book/downloads/Case%20Studies%20in%20Inclusive%20Teaching.pdf, last accessed 6 November 2006.

Stanley, E., and M. Waterman. 2000. LifeLines OnLine: Curriculum and teaching strategies for adult learners. *Journal of College Science Teaching* (March/April): 306–310.

Stanley, Ethel, and M. Waterman. 2005. Investigative cases: Collaborative inquiry in science. *Great Ideas in Teaching Biology* 3: 6–14.

Vohra, Faquir C. 2000. Changing trends in biology education: An international perspective. In Commission on Biology Education. *Biology International* 39. Online at http://www.iubs.org/test/bioint/39/8.htm. Accessed September 29, 2007.

Waterman, Margaret A., and Ethel D. Stanley. 2004. *Investigative case based learning: Teaching Scientifically while connecting science to society.* Invention and Impact: Products of the NSF CCLI Program. Washington, DC: AAAS and NSF Publications.

Younès, Talal. 2000. Biological education: Challenges of the 21st century. Commission on Biology Education. *Biology International* 39. Online at http://www.iubs.org/test/bioint/39/2.htm. Accessed September 29, 2007.

Annotated Preface to the Student Edition

Note to Instructors: Preparing students for investigative cases and collaborative learning is important. Collaborative learning methodologies are gaining popularity in education; however, they are little used in traditional science teaching. When introducing Investigative Case–Based Learning, instructors need to take time to tell students about the new expectations that come with these approaches. Students need to understand that ICBL requires that they will be doing some of the learning on their own. Not all students have experience working effectively in groups. The Preface to the Student Edition provides information on what to expect when using cases. However, students need to know their instructors' individual expectations. Whether you are asking individual students to do a case or asking groups of students to develop their own investigations based on the Case Analysis, share your assessment plan with your students.

Biological Inquiry: A Workbook of Investigative Cases is a book of short cases (stories or scenarios) based on decisions people face in everyday life that require familiarity with biological concepts. Each case is designed to complement a related unit in *Biology*, 8th edition, by Campbell and Reece. These investigative cases provide opportunities for you to apply the biology you are learning in the classroom to realistic situations.

Your instructor may use the cases in a variety of ways during your course. For example, the cases could be assigned as homework, integrated into a lecture, or incorporated into a laboratory. You might work alone or in groups. Working in groups can give you insight into the way scientists work because real-world scientific investigations often involve collaboration. Even if you are not planning on becoming a scientist, it is important to understand the way scientists work in order to better grasp biological issues that affect you as a global citizen.

Regardless of the way your instructor chooses to use this book, this preface will give you some general advice and insight into learning with cases.

(1) What is a case?

A case is a type of scenario that is useful for learning. In general, cases are created in many formats including videos, computer-based programs, and written forms. Text-based cases, such as the ones in this book, are common and they can be one paragraph or many pages long. In this book, the cases are about a page long.

Following is an example of a short biology case similar to ones you will find in this book.

> Case: *Derrick's Malaise*
> About a month after returning home from a season of fieldwork in Guatemala, Derrick began to feel sick again. His roommate took him to the clinic. They were both worried that he was having a recurrence of the malaria he had contracted on the trip.

"How could I have these symptoms again?" Derrick asked the resident, Dr. Welty. "I finished the prescription they gave me in Guatemala and I have been feeling fine."

"I'm not sure why you have this again." Dr. Welty replied. "We'll need a blood sample so we can analyze the organism to see what strain it is. In the meantime, let's try a different drug. I'm going to switch you to chloroquine." He continued, "You know, malaria is one of the most common infectious diseases in the world. I've got some contacts at the CDC who may be interested in your relapse. May I share your records with them?"

"I wonder if I can get malaria from Derrick?" wondered Derrick's roommate, who was flipping through magazines in the waiting room.

Case Authors: Ethel Stanley and Margaret Waterman, 2001. Investigative Cases and Case Based Learning in Biology, version 1.0. in Jungck and Vaughan (Eds.) BioQUEST Library VI. San Diego: Academic Press.

(2) How do I begin?

Begin by finding out what the case is about. Read through the case to get a sense of the story and issues. If you are working in a group, try having one person read the case out loud while the others read along silently. This may sound unusual, but it helps everyone in the group focus on the case.

Note to Instructors: Consider reading the case as a whole class. You might project the case or have students open their book to the case. Ask for student volunteers to read the case aloud. (No more than a couple of paragraphs per student is a good idea.) Then ask, "What is this case about?" Let 5–7 people answer. Accept responses or ask for clarification, but do not start lecturing. You may be surprised at the range of answers you hear. Next ask if anyone has any experience with the topics related to the case. For example, if you were using our sample case, Derrick's Malaise, *you could ask: "Does anyone have any experience with malaria?" "Has anyone had shots before traveling in the tropics?" "How can you prevent mosquito bites?" These questions get the students to think about what they already know.*

(3) What is the Case Analysis all about?

Once your group has read the case, go to the Case Analysis sheet found just after each case. Case Analysis helps you to identify the main ideas in the case, as well as what you already know about the situation, and what your questions are about the case. If you analyze the case in a group, you will share your ideas, hear what others are thinking, and have a good sense of what the group needs to learn about this case. Case Analysis involves four steps.

Note to Instructors: *We strongly recommend that students do the Case Analysis in small groups of 4–10. When students share their ideas, several things happen. They become aware of what they already know and what they don't know. They learn from others. In a peer group, students are more likely to share their ideas, especially ones they are not certain of, including misconceptions. If you are teaching an online course, consider doing the Case Analysis in a chat room or bulletin board.*

Step A. Recognize potential issues and major topics in the case.

Go back and read the case again, this time highlighting or underlining words or phrases that seem to be important to understanding the situation. Look for issues that you might explore further. Jot down your ideas and questions about these words and phrases. If you are working in a group, this approach might be done as a group discussion, with one person keeping a list of issues as they are raised. At this point, you are also answering the question "What is this case about?"

The following are examples of some of the kinds of issues raised in the case *Derrick's Malaise*.

> **What does the case seem to be about?** Malaria, how it is caused, why it might reoccur, how it is treated, and how it is transmitted.
>
> **What are some potential issues?** How malarial drugs work, Derrick's relapse, worldwide rates of malarial infections, the role of the CDC

Step B. What specific questions do you have about these topics?

Note to Instructors: *For this section, we also recommend that you break the class into groups of 4–10 students and have them brainstorm the Know/Want to Know chart for 5 to 10 minutes. As you walk around and listen to the groups, you may hear wrong information. Usually this misinformation will get sorted out as the students continue their work in the unit, or someone else in the class may provide the correction. Don't stop a group to correct wrong information. After most students seem finished, bring the class back together and ask for a few items in the "What Do I Know?" and the "What Do I Need to Know?" columns. Groups can share their thinking with the larger class. Case Analysis discussions often serve as segues to lectures that will link to many of the questions the students have asked. These discussions also provide opportunities to introduce labs that go with the topics raised in the cases.*

In this step of Case Analysis, you will share what you already know or what you think you know and you will raise your questions. The "Know/Need to Know" chart, found in each Case Analysis, is a way to organize your thoughts. An example is included below.

Use Case Analysis as a brainstorming session. You can refer back to the underlined words and phrases in the case as a way to help organize this discussion. This step can be accomplished alone; however, experience shows it is better done in a group.

Using the *Derrick's Malaise* case as an example, here are some questions raised by learners who have worked with this case:

What Do I Know?	What Do I Need to Know?
• Malaria is transmitted by mosquitoes.	• Why was Derrick in Guatemala?
• It is found in locations that are warm and damp.	• How common is malaria—worldwide, Guatemala, United States?
• It isn't common today in the United States.	• What role does the CDC have?
• It can be treated with drugs.	• What kind of organism causes malaria?
• You can get better.	• Should Derrick's roommate be concerned?
• It can recur (from the case).	• What is chloroquine? Is it a common drug? How does it work? Is it safe?
• It is caused by a microorganism.	• What other drugs are used?
• The CDC is the Centers for Disease Control and Prevention.	• How do you prevent malaria?
• Many people die of malaria each year.	• Do all types of mosquitoes transmit malaria?
	• What strains of the malarial organism are there?
	• Is it OK for the doctor to switch drugs without knowing more?

Step C. Assign priority to the questions.

Review the questions listed on the "What Do I Need to Know?" side of the chart. It is very likely that your brainstorming session raised many different kinds of questions on many topics related to the case (but not necessarily to biology). Go over your list and put a check by the three questions that seem most important to understanding this case. One way to do this is to think about which questions fit with the topics on your course syllabus or in the textbook chapters being studied. Check off those questions as well as others that interest you the most.

> If *Derrick's Malaise* was introduced while you were reading a chapter on microorganisms, questions about the organism causing malaria would be fairly important to investigate. Other questions that you find interesting but are not linked to a syllabus topic may also be chosen for study, such as, how does chloroquine work?

You will find that some of your questions may be addressed in the investigations that accompany the case. You might also have questions that this case book does not address. Your instructor might suggest that you expand on these questions by developing a paper, presentation, experiment, ethics statement, or other product.

Note to Instructors: You might want to find out what the students thought were their most relevant questions. This might be useful information to integrate into the course at some point. In any event, asking students to decide on the most important questions helps to foster an essential learning skill—prioritizing their own learning.

"One of the greatest challenges in biology is to frame appropriate and productive questions that can be pursued by the technology at hand. You have probably had a great deal of experience in solving pre-posed problems, such as those found at the end of textbook chapters. However, if you were asked to go into a lab or out in a field and pose a research question, you will find that this is often difficult to do without some practice . . ."

(The BioQUEST Library IV: *A Note to the Student.* University of Maryland Press, 1996)

Step D. What kinds of references or resources would help you answer or explore these questions?

No matter what questions you investigate, it is likely you will seek and use resources to help you develop persuasive answers. It is important to develop the habit of thinking broadly about where you might go to find answers to your questions. Resources may include your textbooks, other library materials, computer simulations, results of lab or field research, articles, data sets, maps, e-mails, pamphlets from organizations, interviews with experts, or museum exhibits. Be creative, but remember your data are only as good as your sources.

For *Derrick's Malaise*, you might choose to examine

- Maps of malaria prevalence
- A reference book such as *Physicians' Desk Reference* to find out how chloroquine works
- A Web page from the CDC with international travel precautions
- Your textbook index for relevant terms
- A simulation in which the prevalence of different species of competing mosquitoes is examined under different conditions
- An interview with a person who has had malaria

You will find links to a variety of online resources referenced in the cases on the Campbell website (http://www.campbellbiology.com) under the tab marked "Case Book." In addition to the resources organized by case, you will find additional open-ended investigations where you can pose your own questions.

Note to Instructors: *To reduce the time students spend looking for information, you might choose to put some text materials on reserve in the library, make a page of relevant Web links, or have resources immediately available in the classroom or online. We are always pleased to hear some of the unusual sources of information students suggest. Sometimes this is an opportunity to discuss the quality of information.*

(4) What do I do after the Case Analysis?

Each case is accompanied by several investigations. Your instructor might assign just one or two of the available investigations, depending on what fits best in your course. You can also use this book independently. You might complete the Case Analysis and selected investigations as a way to check your own knowledge.

Note to Instructors: We really do expect you to pick and choose among the investigations offered or to use only the case as a way to open up a new topic in class. There are more investigations in each chapter (and more on the Case Book website) than we expect any instructor to use in one course. You will find a comprehensive article on ways to use investigative cases in college science courses online at http://serc.carleton.edu/introgeo/icbl/index.html.

(5) What if my instructor wants me to develop my own investigations?

Your group is likely to raise different questions in the case analysis from the ones investigated in this book. Sometimes an instructor might ask you to follow up your own question in a lab or to design an investigation of your choice. Following is some advice on ways to turn your case-related questions into scientific investigations.

Note to Instructors: Again, we refer you to http://serc.carleton.edu/introgeo/icbl/index.html for much more information on guiding students to open-ended investigations related to a case.

A. Getting started: How do I develop my question?

As you develop the problem and questions you want to use to investigate and learn more about the topics, it will be important for you to consult with others, such as members of your group or other classmates. Discussing your ideas and plans is an important step in refining problems and can lead you to different perspectives and possible good research problems. Continue this practice of sharing with others as you gather evidence for your problem and as you prepare to present your conclusions. This kind of communication is the standard among scientists.

B. What am I expected to do with my question(s)?

Once you have a problem you want to investigate, you and your instructor might consider any of the following:

- Design and conduct new investigations utilizing laboratory or field methods.
- Use computer software modules, spreadsheets, simulations, data sets, interactive maps, remote sensing, or graphics to investigate the question.
- Seek new sources of data (further references, interviews, data sets).
- Develop an investigation that builds from a standard lab exercise, perhaps by changing the independent variable or establishing new controls.

Following are three possible investigations for *Derrick's Malaise*.

1. Work with a simulation to investigate hypotheses about control of mosquitoes that carry malaria-causing organisms. Nonvector mosquitoes can be introduced to compete with the vectors.

2. Use genomics tools and the PlasmoDB (a database of gene sequences from many species of *Plasmodium*) to examine genes in resistant and nonresistant strains of *Plasmodium falciparum*.

3. Develop an experiment to test the effectiveness of controlling mosquito populations with fish that feed on larvae.

Note to Instructors: There are many ways to engage students in scientific inquiry. Students might be asked to design their own experiments from scratch. Alternatively, the instructor may provide the structure of an inquiry experience in its entirety. Or an instructor could take a middle-of-the-road approach by telling students about available materials and procedures but allowing the students to develop their own experiments. The instructor may play an active role by introducing specific lab activities, equipment, or methodologies, or by introducing students to simulations, data sets, or modeling programs that relate to key questions raised by the case. Again, it is up to the instructor to decide how open-ended he or she wishes the investigations to be. Many of the faculty using cases initiate inquiry by starting with lab and field activities with which students are familiar. They ask students to build on prior knowledge as they alter variables or methods and implement their own experiments.

C. When am I finished?

". . . You must confront the issue of closure in research. How do you know when you have a 'right' answer? When is research done? Scientists do not arrive at a final answer; usually research is abandoned for a variety of reasons, including time, resources, and most importantly when the scientific research team is 'satisfied' with their conclusions, that is when the solution is "useful" for some purpose."

(The BioQUEST Library IV: *A Note to the Student.* University of Maryland Press, 1996)

When you are ready to present your conclusions, remember that you need to persuade others of the value of your methodologies and data. Consider your audience carefully as you develop products to support your conclusions, such as

- scientific posters
- advertisements urging political action
- videos defining the issues for the public
- pamphlets/brochures with recommendations for a specific user group
- consulting reports (if you are role-playing)
- art work, such as cartoons, revealing issues from the case

- designs for a new technological approach to the problem
- scientific reports to local or regional groups
- a new case study to emphasize your findings

> "Research is not complete, no matter how many experiments have been conducted, no matter how many puzzles have been solved, until peers outside of a research team are persuaded of the utility of the answers. Persuasion is a social process and an essential one for you to experience in order to understand the nature of scientific theories and paradigm shifts. Communication in the science community is an active process full of controversy and debate. The productive side of science involves open criticism of the methods and conclusions made by a research group. This controversy and debate is important to the creation and acceptance of new scientific knowledge."
>
> (The BioQUEST Library IV: *A Note to the Student*. University of Maryland Press, 1996)

D. How will our group work be assessed and evaluated?

Like many students, you probably have concerns about the assessment and evaluation methods used in group work, especially in scientific inquiry.

Peer review is a key feature of how scientists judge each other's work. With investigative cases, you are likely to peer review one another's proposals, investigations, and persuasive materials. Recently, self-assessment has become a more frequent component of assessment in science, especially as more group work is done.

There are many ways to assess group products and group processes. Some instructors give a group grade and an individual grade. Other instructors include either peer evaluations or group self-evaluations in the grading process. If your instructor has not already explained how you will be assessed, you might want to discuss this.

Note to Instructors: The way in which students are tested is the most significant factor in how they will approach learning in a course. To encourage collaboration, it is important to assess collaboration. The use of ICBL allows instructors to assess learning throughout the process, not only by the final student product.

There are many informal opportunities to assess the performance of students who use investigative cases. You may make observations on individuals and groups at work, evaluate the quality of problem-solving approaches, or ask specific questions about process so students identify and assess the strategies employed by their group. Activities that students engage in as they work on ICBL cases and investigations include

- *participation and contribution to work in groups*
- *identification of issues*
- *development of questions*
- *proposal of investigations*
- *location of resources*

- *carrying out investigations*
- *production of materials*
- *presentations*

During any of these activities, you may wish to assess your students or just inform them that they are

- *actively acquiring information about an appropriate topic within this problem space.*
- *reorganizing this information.*
- *using strategies to select resources beyond text materials.*
- *using a problem-oriented approach.*
- *collaborating with other individuals in problem posing or problem solving.*
- *choosing among alternative approaches to solve problems.*
- *negotiating, arguing, or attempting to convince others.*
- *generating graphs, tables, charts, or other graphics.*
- *presenting conclusions.*
- *presenting evidence to support their conclusions.*
- *generating further questions as a result of this activity.*

(6) Why are cases a good way to learn biology?

An important goal of biology education is that you be able to apply what you learn within courses to your life. Scientific problem solving is a valuable tool, in both professional and everyday life. It is important for you to do science as well as learn about it. And it is important for you to choose the problems to be studied and the resources you will use as you investigate those problems.

By doing investigative cases, you engage in scientific inquiry. You will read critically, pose questions, analyze data, think critically, construct hypotheses, investigate options, interpret results, and communicate scientific arguments. No matter how your instructor chooses to use this book, investigative cases can be a useful and interesting tool in your study of biology.

Credits

Fig. 1.5: Figure adapted from www.ftns.wau.nl/agridata/starchpackfoam.htm.

Figs. 2.2 and 2.3: From E. D. Stanley et al., "Modeling wine fermentation," pp. 85–92 and software on CD-ROM. In J. R. Jungck et al., *Microbes Count!* Beloit, WI: BioQUEST Curriculum Consortium and American Society for Microbiology Press, 2003. Used with permission.

Figs. 4.2 and 4.4: W. Herb Wagner, 2001. "Dendrogrammaceae." In E. D. Stanley, *Visual Data Sets,* BioQUEST Library VI, San Diego: Academic Press. Used with permission.

Fig. 4.6: From H. A. Ross et al., 2003. DNA surveillance: Web-based molecular identification of whales, dolphins, and porpoises. *Journal of Heredity* 94: 111–114. Copyright © 2003 American Genetic Association. Used with permission.

Figs. 4.8 and 4.10: David Hornack and Sam Donovan, from http://bioquest.org/bedrock/problem_spaces/whippo/background.php. Copyright © 2004 BioQUEST Curriculum Consortium. All Rights Reserved. Used with permission.

Fig. 5.1: www.scotese.com/gzelclim.htm. © 2000, PALEOMAP Project.

Fig. 6.5: From D. J. Caffrey, *The European Corn Borer Farmers' Bulletin,* FB1046, USDA.

Fig. 6.8: Adapted from art provided courtesy of National Corn Growers Association.

Table 6.1: From http://www.uky.edu/Agriculture/Entomology/entfacts/fldcrops/ef118.htm. Courtesy of Ric Bessin, Extension Entomologist, University of Kentucky.

Fig. 7.3: Adapted from M. E. Ensminger and C. G. Olentine. *Feeds and Nutrition.* Clovis, Calif.: The Ensminger Publishing Company, © 1978.

Fig. 8.4: From http://mddnr.chesapeakebay.net/eyesonthebay/index.cfm. Map used with the courtesy of the Maryland Department of Natural Resources. www.dnr.maryland.gov.

Fig. 8.5: From http://www.cbrsp_toc_mb_chl_page.htm. This site is hosted by the Horn Point Laboratory at the University of Maryland Center for Environmental Science. Used with permission.

Figs. 9.2a: Data Source: World Organisation for Animal Health (OIE) and national governments. Map production: Public Health Mapping and GIS Communicable Diseases (CDS). Adapted from World Health Organization. © WHO 2007. All rights reserved.

Photo Credits

Instructor's Edition Contents

Chapter 1:

Picture Perfect

INSTRUCTOR'S GUIDE

As with all the cases in this book, please read the preface if you have not already done so. In the preface you will find suggestions for using Investigative Case Based Learning (ICBL) in different instructional situations such as starting a new lecture topic, assessing what students already know, setting a context for lab activities, and so on. The preface also describes ways to use cases in a variety of classroom settings and suggests multiple ways to assess learning with cases.

Picture Perfect accompanies Unit One: The Chemistry of Life in Campbell and Reece's *Biology*, 8th edition. The case emphasizes material covered in Chapter 5: The Structure and Function of Large Biological Molecules. Students begin the investigative case by reading a narrative about a museum conservator preserving a 19th-century cotton dress stained with starch. There are three strands (or themes) in the case:

- The use of scientific thinking in preservation work
- The structure and function of polysaccharides, with an emphasis on starch and cellulose
- The introduction of amylase as an enzyme that catalyzes the hydrolysis of starch

Students should complete the Case Analysis immediately following the reading of the case. We strongly suggest that students work in groups to complete the Case Analysis. Actively listening to and challenging the ideas of others can help learners become aware of their own misconceptions, yet also value their own and others' prior knowledge.

Five investigations accompany *Picture Perfect*. Three are "core" investigations relating directly to the facts of the case, and two are additional investigations that extend the case to other applications. Table IG1.1 describes what students will gain from each investigation. See the Case Book website for an additional investigation on plants used as food starch globally.

Table IG1.1 Picture Perfect Case Overview.

Investigation	Learning Goals	Inquiry Skills Used
Core Investigations		
I. Critical Reading	Students read parts of Chapter 5 covering an introduction to macromolecules, carbohydrates, and proteins. They also read selected sections in Chapter 8 about enzyme function. Emphasis is on carbohydrate chemistry and enzymes specific to starch.	• identifying information relevant to a question • making observations and constructing an evidence-based argument • relating structure to function
II. Analyze and Design an Experiment A. Analyzing an Experiment	Using data generated by simulation software in the *Chapter 41, Investigation: What Role Does Amylase Play in Digestion?* found on the Campbell Biology website or CD-ROM, students analyze the experimental setup and interpret outcomes. The use of iodine to test for starch and Benedict's solution to test for simple sugars is featured.	• analyzing experimental setups and data • explaining outcomes of experiments
B. Designing an Experiment	Students use the same experimental methods employed in II.A. to test a variable of their choice. They design experimental and control treatments and predict results. Students could use the website software to run their experiment (optional).	• writing questions • writing hypotheses • identifying variables • designing treatments • predicting results
III. Off the Wall: Starch Degradation Investigation	Students study a realistic situation in which an individual needs to test methods of removing wallpaper paste.	• interpreting visual data • making decisions • applying concepts of experimental design and starch chemistry
Additional Investigations		
IV. Structure and Function of Starch A. Kinds of Starch	Students examine micrographs of starch granules from different plants. They infer the kind of starch Rob removed from the dress in the case.	• making observations • using evidence to solve problems
B. Using Starches in Food	Students learn the stages in starch gelatinization and apply their knowledge to common errors in preparing gravy and mashed potatoes.	• reading graphs • applying structure-function thinking to common problems
C. How Structural Properties of Native and Modified Starches Affect Their Function	Students learn how amylose affects the properties of native and modified starches, and how these differences are used in manufacturing starch-based products.	Students apply the concepts of starch structure and function to determine the best types of starch to use in the production of different foods.

| V. Open-Ended Investigations | Students transfer their knowledge of starch to a new example. | • locating and managing information
• identifying how their knowledge applies |

Table IG1.2 contains several resources related to *Biology*, 8th edition, that will help your students further their understanding of this case. Note that chapter readings and activities are listed in order of importance.

Table IG1.2 Campbell-Related Resources.

Resource	Chapter/Activity	Topics Covered/Activity Titles
Critical Reading from *Biology*, 8th edition	Chapter 5: Structure and Function of Large Biological Molecules	Formation and breakdown of macromolecules; carbohydrates and proteins (Concepts 5.1–5.3)
	Chapter 8: An Introduction to Metabolism	Substrate specificity of enzymes; effects of local conditions on enzyme activity (Concept 8.4)
Related readings from *Biology*, 8e	Chapter 2: The Chemical Context of Life	Hydrogen bonds; molecular shape and function (Concept 2.3)
	Chapter 4: Carbon and the Molecular Diversity of Life	Carbon skeleton variation and molecular diversity (Concept 4.2)
Campbell website/ CD-ROM	Chapter 5 **Activities**	Models of Glucose Carbohydrates
	Chapter 8 **Activity**	How Enzymes Work
	Chapter 2 **Activity**	Hydrogen Bonds
	Chapter 41 **Investigation**	What Role Does Amylase Play in Starch Digestion?
	Chapter 2 **Investigation**	How Are Space Rocks Analyzed for Signs of Life?
	Chapter 3 **Activity**	The Polarity of Water
Morgan/Carter *Investigating Biology*, 6e	Lab Topic 4	Enzymes: A helpful introduction to enzyme function. In Exercise 4.3, students test the influence of concentration, pH, and temperature on amylase activity.

Case Narrative

Students were asked to underline terms or phrases in the introductory narrative that they think are important to understanding the case. Suggested terms and phrases that students might have chosen are in bold type.

As she drove back to the museum, Bryn considered the box and the tiny dress it contained. It had been worn by a child in a **19th-century portrait** of a local family already owned by the museum. Discovered in a trunk **in an unheated barn** by descendants, the dress was in **surprisingly good condition**.

Once she arrived, Bryn went to the curators' workroom to give the dress to Rob, the museum's **textile conservator**. Seeing Rob working intently, she quietly knocked on the half-open door. He put down his tools and looked up.

"Rob," she said excitedly. "Here it is! The dress I told you about from the painting! The donor was about to have it cleaned, but I'm so glad he called here first."

"You're not kidding. **It's easy to ruin old fabrics**," Rob said as he accepted the box with the tissue-wrapped dress. After **putting on gloves**, he unwrapped the old dress carefully and **laid it flat** on a **clean table** to examine it. He saw that the cotton dress was **slightly yellowed** and there was a **small, stiff stain** near the neckline. He wondered if that spot might prove troublesome. "This is terrific, Bryn. I'll do my magic, and with luck these discolorations and spots should disappear."

Bryn laughed, knowing that Rob's work had nothing to do with **magic or luck**. As she left the workroom, Rob grabbed an *Object Description and Restoration* form and began to **fill it out in pencil**. Next he gently brushed the dress. Using a metal probe, he **scraped the stain** at the neckline and placed the **sample on a microscope slide**. Rob examined the slide with the microscope, noticing **several granules** mixed in with a few longer fibers. He was not surprised to see **long cellulose fibers, which he knew to be cotton**. The granules, though, which were smooth and oval-shaped with a diameter of about $75\,\mu m$ (micrometers), came from the stain itself. He added a drop of a weak, yellowish **iodine solution** to the slide. The **granules turned dark blue.** Under *Treatment Plan* he wrote "Neckline stain: **use amylase cleaning solution**"—an **enzymatic solution specific for removing starch**.

Suggested Answers for Case Analysis

1. **Recognize potential issues and major topics in the case.** What is this case about? Underline terms or phrases that seem to be important to understanding this case. Then list **3 or 4** biology-related topics or issues in the case.

   Biology-related topics or issues: how museum textile conservators work, starch and its removal, cellulose, enzymes.

2. **What specific questions do you have about these topics?** By yourself, or better yet, in a group, make a list of what you already know about this case in the "What Do I Know?" column. List questions you would like to learn more about in the "What Do I Need to Know?" column.

   There are many possible answers, depending on the experiences of your students. Below are some likely responses:

What Do I Know?	What Do I Need to Know?
• *Iodine turns starch granules blue.* • *In plants starch forms granules.* • *In plants cellulose forms long fibers.* • *Enzymes can clean stains.* • *Fabrics (such as cotton) can last for a long time in poor storage conditions.*	• *What do the granules and fibers look like?* • *What does starch look like?* • *How does one become a textile conservator?* • *How does amylase work?*

3. Put a check mark by **1–3** questions or issues in the "What Do I Need to Know?" list that you think are most important to explore.

   You should expect a range of responses. Most students will use the contextual clues of being in a biology class and beginning the chemistry unit to identify chemistry-related questions.

4. **What kinds of references or resources would help you answer or explore these questions?** Identify two different resources and explain what information each resource is likely to give that will help you answer the question(s). Choose specific resources.

   Accept any reasonable resource (e.g., text, other book, Internet sites, data tables, and so on) that could be related to this case. The answer "the Web" is too vague. Students should explain the type of site they are looking for or search terms they might use.

Suggested Answers for Core Investigations

I. Critical Reading

To complete this investigation, you should have already read Concepts 5.1–5.3 in Chapter 5. In Concept 8.4, you should also read the text under the headings "Substrate Specificity of Enzymes" and "Effects of Local Conditions on Enzyme Activity." Then answer the following questions.

1. In the case narrative, Rob learned that the stain near the neckline of the dress contained starch. What specific types of macromolecule are starch and cellulose?

   Starch and cellulose are polysaccharides (carbohydrates).

2. What monomer is found in starch and cellulose?

   glucose

3. Contrast the structure and function of starch with those of cellulose in plant cells.

   Starch is a storage carbohydrate made of glucose monomers that are used for cellular fuel. The glucose monomers in amylose are joined by 1–4 linkages. Amylopectin, a branched polymer, has 1–4 linkages at its straight points and 1–6 linkages at branch points. All the glucose monomers in starch are in the a configuration.

   Cellulose is a building material found in plant cell walls. It is also made of glucose monomers, but its glycosidic linkages are different from those of starch. The glucose monomers of cellulose are all in the b configuration, making every other glucose monomer upside down in relation to the others. The molecules can form hydrogen bonds with other parallel cellulose molecules. This property allows for the formation of the strong fibers found in plant cell walls.

4. What is an enzyme?

   Enzymes are proteins that regulate metabolism by acting as catalysts (chemical agents that selectively speed up chemical reactions in the cell without being consumed by the reaction). Enzymes recognize and bind only to their specific substrates (the substances a particular enzyme works on).

5. To remove the stain from the dress, Rob treated the stain with a cleaner containing the hydrolytic enzyme *amylase*. Explain what happens to starch at the molecular level when it is acted upon by amylase. You may wish to sketch the structure of starch to show how this enzyme works (see Figure 5.7 in your text).

   As a hydrolytic enzyme, amylase breaks apart starch by adding a water molecule and breaking apart the 1–4 glycosidic linkages. A hydrogen atom is added to one monomer and an OH molecule to the other monomer involved in a single bond. Expect students' drawings to resemble Figure 5.5a, Dehydration synthesis of maltose in reverse.

6. Under the right conditions, amylase breaks down amylose efficiently; however, the enzyme is not very effective in breaking down amylopectin. Examine Figure 5.6 and read the related text in your textbook. Use your observations to propose a hypothesis for why amylase breaks down amylose much more effectively than amylopectin.

   Amylose is a starch made of glucose molecules bound together in 1–4 glycosidic linkages. Amylopectin has these same linkages, but it also has 1–6 glycosidic linkages, which are not broken down by amylase. Therefore, amylopectin is only partially degraded by amylase.

7. Explain why Rob did not have to worry that the amylase cleaning solution would damage the dress.

Amylase is specific for a configuration, 1–4 glycosidic linkages. Cellulose consists of b linkages; therefore, it is not a substrate of amylase. Rob knew that the dress was made of cotton, which consists mainly of cellulose, and would not be affected by amylase.

II. Analyze and Design an Experiment

To further investigate starch and its components, first you will analyze an experiment. Then you will design your own. The experiment you will analyze was performed using the software in the *Chapter 41, Investigation: What Role Does Amylase Play in Digestion?* found on the Campbell website (http://www .masteringbio.com) and CD-ROM. However, you can complete the exercise with the information provided in this workbook.

A. Analyze an Experiment. In the following controlled experiment, we used both iodine solution (IKI) and Benedict's solution as indicators to test the effect of amylase on starch. As you may recall, Rob used the indicator iodine to test the dress stain for the presence of starch.

The Experiment: Four test tubes were set up. To find out which substances were placed in each tube, see the table in the bottom section of Figure 1.2. The tubes were then incubated at 37°C for 60 minutes (none were boiled). Half of the contents in tubes 1–4 were poured into tubes 1A–4A. The contents of tubes 1A–4A were tested with IKI. The remaining contents in tubes 1–4 were tested with Benedict's solution. The next set of questions asks you to analyze the results of both tests.

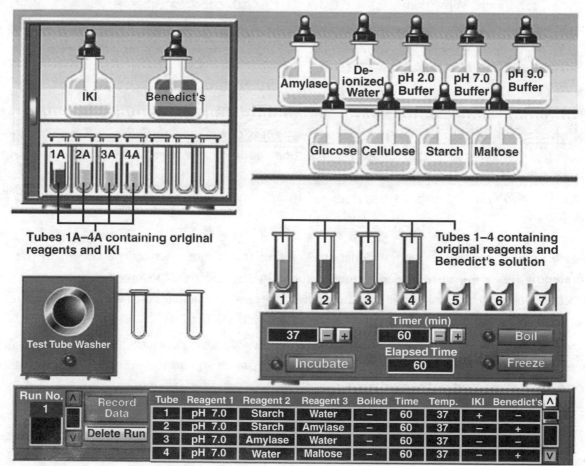

Figure 1.2 Experimental setup and results.

1. Review Figure 1.2 and note which of the reagents were used in each of the four test tubes. In Table 1.1, check off the reagents found in each tube.

   Students should have placed check marks in the areas indicated in Table IG1.3.

Table IG1.3 Answers to Student Table 1.1.

Reagent	Test Tube			
▨▨▨▨	1	2	3	4
Starch	√	√		
Amylase		√	√	
Buffer pH 7.0	√	√	√	√
Maltose				√
Water	√		√	√

2. Note the test-tube results for the use of IKI. The color change in the contents of each test tube is also shown in the test-tube rack at the upper left corner of the figure. A dark shade indicates a positive iodine reaction (the actual color is dark blue) and a light shade indicates a negative reaction (the actual color is yellow). Because Rob used iodine in this case, you know that iodine is a test for starch. Why, then, was the iodine test negative for test tube 2A?

   While test tube 2A did contain starch, amylase was also added to the tube. Amylase broke down the starch during the incubation period; therefore, when iodine is added to the tube there is no starch left for it to react with.

3. What is the purpose of adding iodine to test tubes 1A and 3A?

   Iodine is added to test tube 1A to test the effectiveness of the iodine solution. Because the tube is known to contain starch, the contents of the tube should turn a dark blue. If the color does not change, there may be something wrong with the iodine solution. Test tube 3A is a control to show that a combination of iodine and amylase does not lead to a blue solution. The color should remain light yellow.

4. Now examine the results for the Benedict's solution test. Color changes are shown in the rack containing tubes 1–4 at the middle right. A dark shade indicates a positive test (the actual color is reddish brown). A light shade indicates a negative test (the actual color is blue). Do you think Benedict's solution is a test for starch, amylase, or maltose? Explain.

   Benedict's solution must be a test for maltose. The tests with starch alone and amylase alone produced a negative result. The test with maltose alone and with starch and amylase produced positive results. The Benedict's solution test reveals that amylase does break down starch into maltose.

B. Design Your Own Experiment

1. Using *either* the iodine test or the Benedict's test, design an experiment to examine other factors in the action of amylase on starch. Your experiment should test only *one* of the following variables: pH, incubation temperature, incubation time, boiling, or freezing.

   When evaluating a student's experiment, make sure the student has varied only one reagent or one experimental condition. If the student tests pH level, then incubation time and temperature should be the same for all tubes. If the student varies an environmental condition, then the tubes must contain the same reagents.

   a. What question will you investigate in your experiment?

      A student should state a question that relates the variables being changed to the outcome of the test. For example, does a change in pH level affect how well amylase breaks down starch?

   b. Restate the question as a hypothesis (see Chapter 1 in your textbook for an explanation of forming hypotheses):

      If _____,

      then _____.

      The question should be restated as an "If . . . then" statement. Usually a hypothesis is written as "If the variable I am changing goes up (or down), then the result of the test will go up (or down)." An example of a possible hypothesis could be "If the pH is raised as high as possible, then the enzyme will fail to break down starch."

2. In Table 1.2, describe your experimental treatment in test tube 1. Although it is likely that you will have more than one control tube, describe just one of your controls for test tube 2.

Table 1.2 Test Tube Contents and Conditions.

Reagents	Test Tube 1 (experimental)	Test Tube 2 (control)
Starch		
Amylase		
pH		
Experimental conditions		
Incubation time		
Incubation temperature		
Boiling		
Freezing		

The students should fill in the table with the reagents and experimental conditions that will be used in their experimental and control tubes. For the example described in 1.b., test tube 1 would be identical to test tube 2 except for the pH of the buffer.

3. In Table 1.3, indicate the results you would expect if your hypothesis were supported (use "+" and "−" for the test indicator that you chose).

Table 1.3 Predicted Results, Supporting Hypothesis.

Tests	Test Tube 1	Test Tube 2
Benedict's		
IKI		

Predicted results will vary based on the students' proposed experiments.

4. In Table 1.4, indicate the results you would expect if your hypothesis were *not* supported (use "+" and "−" for the test indicator that you chose).

Table 1.4 Predicted Results, Not Supporting Hypothesis.

Tests	Test Tube 1	Test Tube 2
Benedict's		
IKI		

Predicted results will vary based on the students' proposed experiments.

5. *Optional.* Conduct the experiment you designed using the software provided in the *Chapter 41, Investigation: What Role Does Amylase Play in Digestion?* found on the Campbell website (http://www.maseringbio.com) or CD-ROM. Turn in a screen capture of the table showing your results. *Note:* Experiments involving IKI tests of cellulose will not give the correct results due to a bug in the software.

Students could use the software program in the Chapter 41, Investigation: What Role Does Amylase Play in Digestion? to run a simulation of their own experiment.

III. Off the Wall: Starch Degradation Investigation

Hildy planned to surprise her parents by remodeling their living room while they were away for the weekend. First she had to remove the wallpaper so that she could paint. When she started scraping at the edge of the dry wallpaper, only a few small pieces came off. "What's up with this wallpaper?" Hildy asked herself. "It's just not coming off!"

Hildy got a spray bottle and filled it with warm water. She sprayed the walls to moisten large areas. After several minutes, she scraped at the wallpaper again. Larger pieces came off this time, but big patches of hardened paste remained. Hildy couldn't spend the whole weekend scraping! She rummaged around the house and found some alcohol and some vinegar.

Unsure of what these substances would do to the walls, she also went out and bought two different types of commercial wallpaper remover. "I wonder which of these will work the best?" she thought.

To test which one would work best, she chose a section of the wall behind the couch and applied the five substances to a 10-cm^2 section of the wall. She labeled each patch to remember which substance had been applied to each square. After 20 minutes, she noted how much wallpaper she could remove with one scrape from each patch. See the results of her experiment in Figure 1.3.

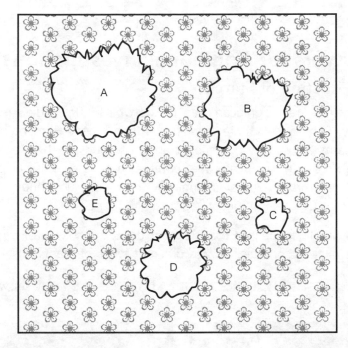

Figure 1.3 The above figure shows a section of Hildy's parents' living room wall after her experiment. The table below is a key containing her results.

Label on Wallpaper	Substance	Approximate % of Wallpaper and Paste Removed
A	remover with 0.5% amylase	100
B	remover with 0.1% amylase	75
C	rubbing alcohol	10
D	vinegar	50
E	water	10

1. Which substance worked best? What does this tell you about the composition of wallpaper paste?

   Substance A, the product with the highest percentage of amylase, allowed the most removal of wallpaper and paste. Wallpaper paste must contain starch.

2. Describe how the most effective substance worked to remove the paste.

   Amylase breaks down the starch in the wallpaper paste by breaking down the 1–4 glycosidic linkages.

3. Considering that vinegar is an acid, explain the results seen with the vinegar.

   Because vinegar is an acid, it slightly hydrolyzes starch, which results in a small clear area.

4. Why was it important that Hildy also test the effect of water alone on the wallpaper paste?

Hildy needed to test the effect of water alone because it is the solvent for the other potential removers. She used water as the control in her experiment to show that water alone cannot break down starch to the same extent as some of the other products.

Suggested Answers for Additional Investigations

IV. Structure and Function of Starches

A. Kinds of Starch. Starches are a significant part of the typical human diet, making up 40–80% of total energy intake. Some plants store more starch than others. Humans have discovered many varieties of starchy plants that satisfy our hunger and taste buds, such as corn, cassava, and potatoes, originally from South America; sweet potatoes and yams, from tropical Africa and South America; chickpeas, from Turkey; plantains, originally from India; rice, originally from Asia; soybeans, originally from China; and wheat, from the Middle East.

Plants store starch as highly condensed granules that do not dissolve easily in water. The composition and size of these granules vary in different types of plants.

1. Contrast the microscopic starch granules of corn with those of potato, shown in Figure 1.4.

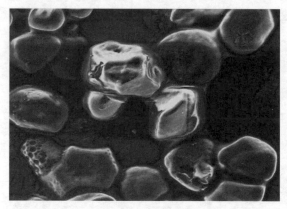 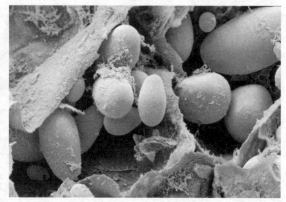

    (a) Starch granules in corn (5–25 μm)   (b) Potato starch (15–100 μm)

Figure 1.4 Note the variations in the size and shape of starch granules.

Corn granules (5–25 μm) generally are smaller than potato granules (15–100 μm). Corn granules are angular and irregularly shaped, while potato granules are smooth and sphere- or oval-shaped.

2. Now that you have learned more about the different types of starch granules, can you infer the type of granules that Rob scraped from the old dress? Explain your response.

Rob most likely scraped off potato starch. The smooth, mostly oval granules were described as being approximately 75 μm in diameter.

B. Using Starches in Food: Understanding Structure for Commercial Application. Although the enzymes in our digestive system are capable of breaking apart starch granules, cooking starchy foods causes the starches to gelatinize, which enhances texture and taste and improves digestion. *Gelatinization* is the process in which granules of starch swell, break up, and disperse in water. Suspensions of various thicknesses are formed during this process.

Figure 1.5 on the next page shows a cornstarch granule before and after gelatinization. (Cornstarch is often used as a thickening agent in food products such as gravies and sauces.) Starch granules have complex structures. The granule surface consists of many amylopectin and some amylose molecules associating tightly with each other due to hydrogen bonding. Water does not easily penetrate the granule. Tiny channels lead from the surface into an amorphous center where less tightly bound amylose and amylopectin molecules are found.

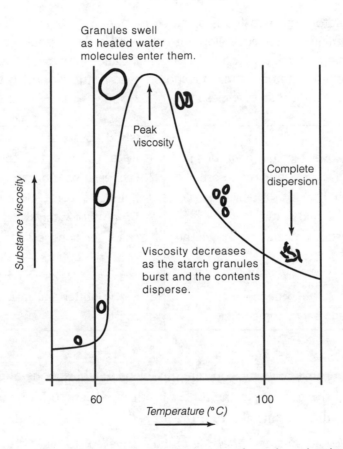

Figure 1.5 Gelatinization and disruption of starch molecules.

When starch granules are immersed in water, two things happen. Water moves slowly through the channels and forms hydrogen bonds with the amylose and amylopectin components in the center of the granules. At the same time, hydrogen bonding among the amylose and amylopectin molecules on adjacent granules causes clumping. Stirring the suspension prevents the granules from forming dense clumps. If understirred, the cornstarch mixture will be lumpy.

When exposed to heat, water molecules move more rapidly. The rapid movement allows more water molecules to enter the granules, causing the granules in the suspension to swell. The cornstarch and water mixture noticeably thickens (increases in viscosity). Because amylose molecules are unbranched, they can easily move through the channels and will leach out of the granules more quickly than amylopectin. If the gel sits and cools at this stage, the amylose molecules will begin to realign by hydrogen bonding, causing the granules to adhere to each other and to the container. The cornstarch may thicken unevenly and the resulting mixture will be difficult to pour.

On the other hand, continued heating of the gelatinized starch transfers more energy to the water molecules, allowing them to further destabilize hydrogen bonds between starch molecules. The granules continue to swell, and more starch molecules leak into the surrounding liquid. Heating past the boiling point causes swollen granules to break into fragments and release all of the starch molecules into the water. At this point, the mixture thins (decreases in viscosity). Stirring the mixture will hasten the thinning process, leading to a runny cornstarch mixture.

Investigation: What Went Wrong?

Gravy and mashed potatoes are two foods prepared in many U.S. homes, but they are tricky to make successfully. Examine the recipes below for gravy and mashed potatoes and answer the following questions using your knowledge of the gelatinization process. (*Hint:* The secret to making gravy and mashed potatoes is maintaining an even distribution of granular structure without fragmenting the individual granules.)

Turkey Gravy	**Mashed Potatoes**
1. In a large saucepan, over medium heat, bring 1 cup of turkey broth and pan juices to a boil.	1. Place a large pot of cold water on the stove.
2. Meanwhile, blend until smooth 2 tablespoons of cornstarch in 1 cup of cold water.	2. Peel each potato, cut into cubes of about 3/4-inch square, and put in the pot.
3. Slowly add the cornstarch mixture to the boiling broth.	3. Do not allow the water to boil too rapidly; check for doneness after 15 minutes.
4. Stir intermittently until the gravy thickens.	4. Mash the potatoes while they are hot. Do not overmash. Never use a food processor.
5. Season to taste with salt and pepper.	5. Mix in butter and milk. Do not let potatoes cool.
6. Remove from heat and serve immediately.	

1. As you begin to prepare turkey gravy, you carefully blend 2 tablespoons of cornstarch into a cup of cold water. You add the mixture to the turkey broth, but then you forget to stir it. Your gravy turns out lumpy. How did the mistake ruin the gravy?

   The cornstarch was allowed to stand after the granules swelled, forming a gel. Amylose molecules leaked out from the center of the granules, causing the granules to adhere to each other and form lumps.

2. To make mashed potatoes, you boil the potatoes for 25 minutes. The potato chunks begin to disintegrate as you drain them. When you add the butter and milk, the potatoes are thin and gluey—similar to wallpaper paste before it dries. What went wrong?

   Overheating broke the potato granules into fragments. The starch molecules are dispersed in the water, with a corresponding decrease in viscosity. The potatoes are therefore thin and watery.

C. Structural Properties of Native and Modified Starches in Commercial Products. Starch has a number of properties that make it useful to manufacturers of prepared foods and other commercial products such as glues. Cornstarch products, such as corn syrup, are among the most common ingredients listed on the food labels of cookies, puddings, frozen dinners, and crackers.

Naturally occurring starches (native starches) may be used in dry form as ingredients for foods (about 75% of wheat flour is starch) or as dry lubricants (baby powder), but most are added to water to create gels and solutions. Two widely used types of native cornstarch, *dent* and *waxy,* vary in their amylose content, which makes them useful for different purposes.

Dent cornstarch comes from the most frequently planted type of corn in the United States. Dent cornstarch usually contains about 80% amylopectin and 20% amylose. Starch products made with dent corn tend to adhere to surfaces and form more rigid layers as they are cooked or allowed to dry. For example, dent cornstarch is used in the production of wallpaper paste. Amylose causes the wallpaper to stick to the wall through hydrogen bonding with cellulose and then to stiffen as it dries. The harder outer coating of jelly beans is also made from dent starch.

Waxy cornstarch is produced by a type of corn plant that does not produce amylose. Waxy starch consists entirely of amylopectin molecules. When this cornstarch is dissolved in a solution, it tends to be more stable than the dent cornstarch. The resulting product pours easily. For example, hot chocolate mixes contain waxy cornstarch.

Manufacturers often chemically modify native cornstarch to form additional bonds that cross-link amylose molecules or cross-link amylose and amylopectin molecules. These modified starches have different chemical properties than the native starches.

- Cross-linked waxy starches like Consista® and Rezista® absorb water but retain their granular structure, producing more stable mixtures with higher viscosity than that found in native starches. Products requiring a thicker consistency, such as gravy in canned stew, often contain modified waxy starch.

- Amylomaize, another modified starch, contains 70% amylose and 30% amylopectin. Manufacturers use amylomaize to make inexpensive and biodegradable packaging foam with good cushioning and resiliency properties. For starch to act like polystyrene (a plastic), its polymer molecules have to align closely through hydrogen bonds. Linear molecules perform better in this way than branched molecules; therefore, the high amylose content of amylomaize makes it work well.

Read the following product description and determine which starch would be the best choice for a manufacturer. (*Note:* The cost of dent starch is low, waxy starch is more expensive, and chemically modified waxy starches are the most expensive. Although cost is always an important factor in manufacturing decisions, for this exercise consider only the characteristics of the different types of starch.)

A. Dent starch   C. Modified waxy starch

B. Waxy starch   D. Amylomaize

1. **Instant cheesecake mix.** Manufacturers need a starch that will maintain a creamy consistency and will neither liquefy nor harden at room temperature. Explain your choice.

   The best choice is C. Modified waxy starch is the best choice because it retains granular structure, producing more stable mixtures with higher viscosity due to cross-linking.

2. **Soups.** Manufacturers need a starch that allows their product to be pourable but does not thicken too much as it cools. Explain your choice.

The best choice is B. Waxy starch is the best choice because it contains only amylopectin. This results in a more stable product that will retain the ability to flow easily when poured.

3. **Batter and breading.** Manufacturers need a starch that will adhere to chicken and then become crunchy as the chicken is cooked. Explain your choice.

The best choice is A. Dent starch is the best choice because amylose molecules are present, enabling the starch product to stick to the chicken through hydrogen bonding and then stiffen.

V. Open-Ended Investigations

A. Why is starch used in paper making? Consider the structure of starch molecules in your answer.

Starch is used throughout the paper-making process. In the wet phases, starch is added to the slumy to improve paper dry strength. Also involved in printability, charge control, and biochem oxygen demand reduction. Starch is also used as a surface application where it increaces strength, improves printability, and increases resistance to grease. Surface starch also acts as a binder, and increased amounts enable a smoother writing surface.

B. See the Case Book website for access to ideas for open-ended student investigations (short- or long-term, group or individual), simulations, and other information on extending your students' learning in this unit.

References

Corn Products U.S. www.cornproductsus.com/MISHRA_STARCH.pdf

Stanley, Keith D., Senior Research Scientist, Tate & Lyle, Decatur, IL. Personal communication.

Tate & Lyle (manufacturer of carbohydrate ingredients) http://www.tateandlyle.com/TateAndLyle/products_applications/product_application_grids/americas/default.htm (accessed June 29, 2007).

Whistler, R. L., and E. F. Paschall. *Starch: Chemistry and Technology.* New York: Academic Press, 1965.

INSTRUCTOR'S GUIDE

As with all the cases in this book, please read the preface if you have not already done so. In the preface you will find suggestions for using Investigative Case Based Learning (ICBL) in different instructional situations such as starting a new lecture topic, assessing what students already know, setting a context for lab activities, and so on. The preface also describes ways to use cases in a variety of classroom settings and suggests multiple ways to assess learning with cases.

Bean Brew accompanies Unit Two: The Cell in Campbell and Reece's *Biology*, 8th edition. The case emphasizes material covered in Chapter 9: Cellular Respiration, with strong links to Chapter 8: An Introduction to Metabolism and Chapter 7: Membrane Structure and Function. There are four strands in the case:

- Fermentation
- Glycolysis
- Enzyme actions
- Osmosis

Students should complete the Case Analysis immediately following the reading of the case. We strongly suggest that students work in groups to complete the Case Analysis. Actively listening to and challenging the ideas of others can help learners become aware of their own misconceptions, yet also value their own and others' prior knowledge.

Five investigations accompany *Bean Brew*. The first three are "core" investigations relating directly to the facts of the case, and two are additional investigations that extend beyond the case itself. Table IG2.1, on the next page, describes what students will gain from each investigation.

Table IG2.1 Bean Brew Case Overview.

Investigation	Learning Goals	Inquiry Skills Used
Core Investigations		
I. Critical Reading	Students use Chapter 9 as their primary resource, with additional information from Chapters 7 and 8 to explain the cellular processes taking place during the production of soy sauce.	• identifying key information • applying generalized information to a specific problem • following a metabolic pathway (glycolysis) and learning to analyze changes to substrates and electron acceptors • interpreting written redox reactions
II. Fermentation of Grapes	Students use output of a model of grape fermentation to further extend their understanding of fermentation. They then apply this information to the case.	• interpreting graphs • applying fermentation and respiration concepts to new situations
III. Alcohol Dehydrogenase	Students explore the enzyme alcohol dehydrogenase and its mode of action in humans and in yeast. They think about reactions in both directions, and consider differences in this enzyme among species.	• drawing two-dimensional chemical structures • examining reactions to identify changes and oxidation/reduction
Additional Investigation		
IV. More Human Uses of Fermentation	Students must meet identified criteria as they prepare a paper discussing a product that undergoes fermentation.	• identifying, evaluating, and managing information, including primary literature • extending general ideas of fermentation to additional specific settings
V. Open-Ended Investigations	Students use free online models of wine fermentation to investigate variables	• identifying variables • designing experiments • interpreting graphs • manipulating a model

Table IG2.2 contains several resources related to *Biology*, 8th edition, that will help your students further their understanding of this case.

Table IG2.2 Campbell-Related Resources.

Resource	Chapter/Activity	Topics Covered/Activity Titles
Critical Reading from *Biology*, 8th edition	Chapter 7: Membrane Structure and Function	Fluidity of membranes (Concept 7.1); effects of osmosis on water balance (Concept 7.3)
	Chapter 8: An Introduction to Metabolism	Catalysis in the active site of enzymes; effects of local conditions on enzyme activity (Concept 8.4)
	Chapter 9: Cellular Respiration: Harvesting Chemical Energy	Redox reactions; the stages of cellular respiration (Concept 9.1); glycolysis (Concept 9.2); fermentation (Concept 9.5); glycolysis connects to other metabolic pathways (Concept 9.6)
Campbell website/ CD-ROM	Chapter 7 **Activity**	Osmosis and Water Balance in Cells
	Chapter 7 **Video**	Plasmolysis
	Chapter 8 **Activity**	How Enzymes Work
	Chapter 9 **Activities**	Glycolysis, Fermentation
Morgan/Carter *Investigating Biology*, 6e	Lab Topic 3	Diffusion and Osmosis
	Exercises 5.1, 5.3	Alcohol Fermentation, Designing and Performing Your Open-Inquiry Investigation

Case Narrative

Students were asked to underline terms or phrases in the introductory narrative that they think are important to understanding the case. Suggested terms and phrases that students might have chosen are in bold type below.

Henry, Edie, Taki, and Sally sat around the table at their favorite restaurant celebrating Henry's new job. "I can't believe it's already been six years since we met," Sally said.

It wasn't long before the talk around the table turned to **biotechnology stocks.** Edie and Taki were always well informed about the latest companies and enjoyed arguing about what products were going to be the "next big thing."

"Excuse me," Sally began with a smile when there was a break in the animated conversation. "What's all the fuss about **a new strain of transgenic fungus?** I can't imagine how this would affect me . . ."

Taki reached for the small **container of soy sauce** on the table and held it up. "It turns out that this fungus will increase the efficiency of the first stage of **brewing soy sauce.** Did you know that brewing soy sauce is one of the **original biotech industries?** They were shipping the stuff **in barrels to Asia** over 500 years ago and **in bottles to Europe** by the 1600s. Now most of the world uses soy sauce."

The friends settled in; considering Taki's usual attention to detail, this would be a long story. "About 5,000 years ago in China," he began, "people grew **soybean crops for food and animal feed. Storing beans was risky** because of spoilage. **Salt was added as a preservative,** but **over time the beans fermented.**"

"Like pickles and sauerkraut?" Henry asked.

Taki nodded and continued, "Except the beans softened as they fermented. This paste was easier to digest, so people started to eat it. Then, about 500 years ago, someone discovered that the **liquid in the bottom of the barrel** could be used for cooking. And so, soy sauce was invented!"

"Is this fermentation process **similar to making wine from grapes?**" Sally asked.

"Well, soy sauce brewing is **actually done in two stages.** In Japan soy sauce is called *shoyu.* To make it, you first **steam the soybeans and mix them with toasted, crushed wheat,** then **add the fungi** *Aspergillus oryzae* and *Aspergillus sojae.* The new mixture, called *koji,* is left uncovered for a couple of days, while the fungi partially digest the soy and wheat."

"So, is the transgenic fungus you were talking about *Aspergillus?*" asked Sally.

"Exactly," Taki replied. "Okay, in the next stage, you **mix the koji with water and a lot of salt** to form a mash called *moromi.* They put the moromi into **airtight containers** and let them **ferment for at least six months.** Squeeze this mash to get the liquid soy sauce, which is **filtered, pasteurized, and tightly bottled.** So that's it—soybeans, wheat, water, salt, and microbes. Back in the days of the empire, they even had special recipes that they made only for the emperor by adding extra flavors."

"So what kind do we have here?" asked Edie.

"Oh, an emperor's brew, for sure," asserted Henry. They all laughed.

Suggested Answers for Case Analysis

1. **Recognize potential issues and major topics in the case.** What is this case about? Underline terms or phrases that seem to be important to understanding this case. Then list **3 or 4** biology-related topics or issues in the case.

   Biology-related topics or issues: biotechnology and new strains of fungi; production of soy sauce; fungal digestion of wheat and soy; fermentation of soy sauce, pickles, sauerkraut, and wine; handling fermented products; role of salt in fermentation

2. **What specific questions do you have about these topics?** By yourself, or better yet, in a group, make a list of what you already know about this case in the "What Do I Know?" column. List questions you would like to learn more about in the "What Do I Need to Know?" column.

   There are many possible answers, depending on the experiences of your students. Below are some likely responses:

What Do I Know?	What Do I Need to Know?
• *Many Asian dishes use soy sauce.* • *The basic processes of making soy sauce. Soy sauce is made of soybeans, wheat, water, salt, and microbes.* • *Some students may have had experience with pickling or preparing other fermented products.* • *You can purchase "lite" or low-salt soy sauce.* • *Microorganisms are needed for fermenting.* • *Fermentation produces alcohol. (Note: Unless they have read Chapter 9, students are unlikely to know that there are several forms of fermentation.)*	• *Does soy sauce contain alcohol?* • *What is the role of salt in fermentation?* • *Why does soy sauce need two production stages?* • *What is happening metabolically in each stage?* • *Why is it difficult for people to digest soybeans?* • *How does fermentation change soy and wheat into soy sauce?* • *Why are microorganisms needed?* • *Why fungi?* • *How could biotechnology improve the fungal strains?*

3. Put a check mark by **one to three** questions or issues in the "What Do I Need to Know?" list that you think are most important to explore.

   You should expect a range of responses. Most students will use the contextual clues of being in a biology class and beginning the cell unit to identify fermentation-related questions.

4. **What kinds of references or resources would help you answer or explore these questions?** Identify two different resources and explain what information each resource is likely to give that will help you answer the question(s). Choose specific resources.

   Accept any reasonable resource (e.g., text, other book, Internet sites, maps, data tables, and so on) that could be related to the case. The answer "the Web" is too vague. Students should explain the type of site they are looking for or search terms they might use.

Suggested Answers for Core Investigations

I. Critical Reading

To complete this investigation, you should have already read Chapter 7: Membrane Structure and Function (specifically Concepts 7.1 and 7.3); Chapter 8: An Introduction to Metabolism (specifically Concept 8.4); and Chapter 9: Cellular Respiration.

A. The Koji Phase. In the koji phase of soy sauce production, fungi produce enzymes that break down the carbohydrate and protein in the soybeans and wheat, thereby obtaining energy and molecules for fungal growth. Recall that koji is left uncovered for a few days, which allows many other types of microbes to enter the soybean-and-wheat mixture.

1. Describe a typical enzyme-substrate complex. What mechanisms do enzymes use to lower activation energy and speed up a reaction?

   Enzymes are proteins that contain a pocket or groove known as the active site. The active site is the area of the enzyme that binds to specific substrate molecules. When substrates are in the active site (forming the enzyme-substrate complex), the enzyme undergoes a conformational change, which brings chemical groups of the active site into positions that enhance their ability to catalyze the chemical reaction. When the reaction is complete, the resulting product molecules are released and the enzyme returns to its previous conformation, ready for the next reaction.

   Enzymes catalyze reactions through a variety of mechanisms. The active site may act as a template, helping two or more reactants become oriented favorably for a reaction to occur. Enzymes may also stretch the substrate molecules toward their transition-state conformation, stressing and bending critical chemical bonds. This reduces the amount of free energy that must be absorbed to achieve a transition state. Alternatively, amino acids in the active site may provide a microenvironment with a pH more favorable to the reaction than exists in the surrounding cell environment. Sometimes the amino acids of the active site briefly form covalent bonds with the substrates as a way to facilitate the reaction.

2. Explain how enzymes break down macromolecules. What is the role of water? What bonds are broken, what bonds are formed? Examine Figure 8.17 as you develop your answer.

   When breaking down macromolecules, the enzyme "holds" the substrate molecule so that the bond between the two building blocks is exposed to water. The enzyme may also place physical stress on these bonds. The bond between two building block molecules (for example, between the C and N of two adjacent amino acids or between the carbons of two adjacent sugars) is broken. As discussed in Chapter 5, these enzymes are involved in hydrolysis reactions. They add a molecule of water to the bond, giving an H to one side of the bond and an OH to the other side. So, at the same time that the bonds between amino acid subunits are being broken, an H is added to the amino side of the peptide bond and a hydroxyl group is added to the carboxyl side of that bond. Similarly, in carbohydrates, an H is added to one side of the glycosidic bond and a hydroxyl to the other.

3. In the koji stage of soy sauce production, *Aspergillus* fungi digest soybeans and wheat. *Aspergillus* uses some of the glucose produced by the breakdown of the carbohydrates to generate ATP through cellular respiration or fermentation. Examine Figure 9.9 and answer the following questions about glycolysis, the first stage of respiration.

a. How many different enzymes shown in Figure 9.9 are used to transform glucose into pyruvate?

10

b. What types of reactions do isomerases catalyze?

Isomerases facilitate the transformation of one type of isomer to another.

c. What kinds of enzymes catalyze reactions that transfer a phosphate group from ATP to another molecule?

kinases

d. If you added an aldolase inhibitor, what key reaction would be unlikely to occur? Explain.

The splitting of fructose-1,6-bisphosphate into two 3-carbon isomers, dihydroxyacetone phosphate and glyceraldehyde-3-phosphate, and all reactions of glycolysis subsequent to that reaction, would be unlikely to occur.

B. The Moromi Phase. Once *Aspergillus* has broken down the macromolecules in the soybeans and wheat into monomers, the koji phase ends. Moromi is then made by mixing the koji with water and enough salt to make a 16–20% concentrated salt solution, or brine.

1. In the moromi phase of soy sauce production, the osmotic conditions for microbes are drastically changed. Sketch a generic cell showing what happens to most cells when they are placed in brine. Explain your sketch. (Hint: Consider the movement of water.)

Students should sketch a shrinking cell showing water moving out of the cell and into the hypertonic environment. Student explanation: Osmosis will occur, causing water in the hypotonic cell to move out into the hypertonic environment.

2. Some microbes have adaptations for osmoregulation in order to live successfully in high-salt environments. When the brine is added, the populations of bacteria and fungi found in the koji change. Do you expect greater or lesser microbial diversity? Why?

The differences in osmolarity in the two environments will cause the death of microorganisms not adapted for high salt concentrations. This is likely to reduce the diversity of microbes in the moromi.

3. Yet another challenge faces the microbes in moromi. After the brine is added, workers place the moromi in airtight containers for several months. Which types of microbes will survive under these conditions? Explain how they will obtain energy for life processes.

The microbes that survive are those that can produce ATP in the absence of oxygen—facultative anaerobes and microbes that are always anaerobic. During fermentation, glycolysis produces ATP. The fermentation cycle continues when pyruvate is converted to a substance that can be reduced by NADH, or pyruvate is reduced by NADH. Without a supply of NAD^+, glycolysis will halt.

4. *Tetragenococcus halophilus* (a bacterium) and *Zygosaccharomyces rouxii* (a fungus) are two facultatively anaerobic species that thrive in moromi. Through fermentation, *Tetragenococcus* produces lactic acid (lactate in its ionized form) and *Zygosaccharomyces* produces ethanol. What molecule is transformed into these waste products? Describe the two processes. What other waste products are produced?

Pyruvate is the molecule transformed into these waste products. In the bacteria performing lactic acid fermentation, pyruvate is reduced by NADH to form lactate. In the fungus, which performs alcohol fermentation, pyruvate is first converted to acetaldehyde (with a release of carbon dioxide as a waste product). Then acetaldehyde is reduced by NADH to ethanol.

5. Are ethanol and lactate oxidized or reduced in these reactions?

They are both oxidized, giving up electrons to NAD[1].

II. Fermentation of Grapes

A. Yeast and Rising Alcohol Concentrations. One of the oldest uses of fermentation by people is to make alcoholic beverages such as wine. However, fermentation also occurs without human intervention. Once grapes ripen on the vine, tiny breaks in the skin of the fruit enable the entry of microbes such as bacteria and fungi. The interior of the grape provides both a high concentration of sugars and low pH. Fermentative yeasts thrive in this environment and metabolize the grape sugars for energy. The products carbon dioxide and ethanol are rapidly transported out of the cells as wastes.

When people make wine by fermenting grapes, the process occurs within an airtight container. Alcohol continues to build up in the container until the alcohol tolerance level of the specific yeast population is reached, ending the fermentation cycle. Figure 2.2 shows the results from a simulation of wine fermentation over a 10-day period.

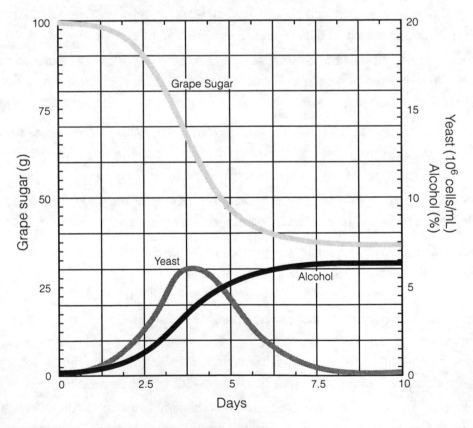

Figure 2.2 Results from a simulation of wine fermentation (Stanley et al., 2003). The graph shows changes in grape sugar, yeast population, and percentage alcohol over a 10-day period. (*Note:* Read grape sugar on the left axis. Yeast and alcohol are shown on the right axis.)

1. Examine Figure 2.2 and fill in the information below.

   a. The grape sugar level starts at _____ g and ends at _____ g.

   100 g; approximately 35 g

   b. The yeast population reaches its highest level of approximately _____ on Day _____.

   6×10^6 cells/mL; Day 4

   c. The alcohol level starts at _____% and ends at approximately _____%.

   0%; 6.4%

   d. Look at the graphs showing the correlation between yeast population and percentage alcohol. At what percentage alcohol does this yeast population begin to decline? _____%

   4%

2. Why isn't the remaining grape sugar converted to ethanol and carbon dioxide?

   When the microorganisms die, the process of fermentation stops.

3. What product of alcohol fermentation is not shown in the preceeding graph?

   carbon dioxide

4. If you removed the alcohol as it was produced, would you predict an increase or a decrease in the amount of grape sugars at 10 days? An increase or decrease in the population of yeast at 10 days? Explain.

   The amount of grape sugar would decrease because high alcohol levels would not kill the yeast. If alcohol were removed, the yeast population would most likely increase until it reached the limit imposed by its food source, at which time the yeast population would decrease.

5. A bottle of wine may spoil if it is allowed to sit for some time after being opened or if its cork does not form a tight seal. Explain what causes the wine to spoil under these conditions. (*Hint:* Available grape sugar declines.)

   Contamination from airborne microbes results in new metabolic activity. The grape sugar is broken down by aerobes using the citric acid cycle and oxidative phosphorylation.

B. Fermentation with Wild and Cultivated Yeasts. In an experiment to identify differences in fermentation carried out by wild and cultivated yeasts, a batch of grapes was divided in two. One batch of grapes was treated with sulfur dioxide to kill wild yeasts before the juice was extracted. The other batch was left untreated, allowing wild yeasts to survive.

   Fermentation of grape juice extracted from these two groups was carried out in separate containers. In the first container, the juice from the treated grapes was inoculated with a special cultivated strain of yeast. The untreated juice in the second container was inoculated with only wild yeast populations. Both containers were allowed to ferment for 10 days. Samples were removed daily to estimate the number of yeast cells and the level of alcohol in each container. Results are shown in Figure 2.3.

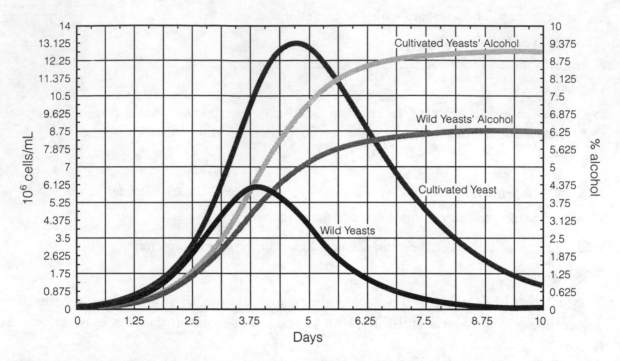

Figure 2.3 Simulated fermentation by wild and cultivated yeasts (Stanley et al., 2003). (*Note:* Read population size on the left axis. Alcohol production is shown on the right axis.)

1. Assuming alcohol level affects the growth of yeast, which yeast has a higher tolerance for alcohol? At approximately what percentage alcohol do the two yeast populations in the different containers begin to decline?

   The cultivated yeast tolerates alcohol at a higher level of about 7.5% alcohol before its population begins to decline. The wild yeast begins to die at about 4% alcohol.

2. Why do you think the alcohol levels increase more rapidly in one of the containers? Use data from Day 3.75 to support your hypothesis.

   More alcohol is produced the greater the number of yeast cells present. If you compare the two containers at Day 3.75, the number of cultivated yeast cells is approximately 10×10^6 as compared to wild yeasts at approximately 6×10^6.

C. **Bottling Soy Sauce.** Now apply some of the concepts you learned about grape fermentation to the Bean Brew case. When soy sauce was first shipped to Europe, Asian soy sauce producers tried the same method they had used for shipping shorter distances within Asia—simply filtering the soy sauce and placing it in non-airtight containers. However, the soy sauce always spoiled before it reached its European destinations! The spoilage problem was solved when the producers started to boil the soy sauce first and then place it in airtight bottles.

1. Explain why placing soy sauce in airtight bottles was more successful for long-distance shipping than simply placing the sauce in barrels.

   Boiling the soy kills the majority of remaining organisms, putting a stop to metabolism. Making the bottles airtight prevents any additional microbes from entering and breaking down molecules in soy sauce for food. Further, any aerobic microorganisms remaining in the soy sauce die once the bottle is sealed. Some fermentation will continue if any anaerobic microbes survive the boiling process.

   In barrels, the soy sauce was only filtered, so there would have been a greater population of surviving microbes, and more microbes could have entered the barrels during shipping. In barrels, the soy sauce would be used for cellular respiration and perhaps further fermentation. For shorter trips within Asia, this method would have worked because the soy sauce would be delivered before the actions of the microbes could cause it to spoil.

2. When the soy sauce was not boiled before it was bottled, the bottles sometimes burst during the voyage. What do you think caused this?

   If a large population of anaerobic organisms were still alive and fermenting, carbon dioxide would build up inside the bottles. The pressure exerted on the bottles by the gas could cause weak or damaged bottles to explode.

3. Bottled soy sauce does not taste the same as fresh soy sauce. What do you think causes this change?

   Boiling the soy sauce for bottling may destroy some of the molecules that enhance the flavor of soy sauce. The possibility of continued fermentation exists because boiling may not have killed all of the organisms. Anaerobes may continue to grow and make products that affect the taste.

4. To preserve flavor in modern times, brewed soy sauces are not boiled but are pasteurized (heated to a temperature of about 60°C [140°F]) before being bottled. Pasteurized soy sauce tastes better than boiled soy sauce. What does pasteurization do? Why should opened bottles of soy sauce be stored in the refrigerator?

   Pasteurization raises the temperature to only 60°C, which is sufficient to kill off many microbes, but not all. Once the soy sauce bottle has been opened, other microbes can get in, and those not killed by pasteurization will continue fermenting. This will occur only if the remaining microbes survive the anaerobic environment. As discussed in Chapter 7, enzymatic proteins may become inactivated at cold temperatures, slowing down both the growth of the microorganisms and the rate of fermentation.

III. Alcohol Dehydrogenase

Ethanol, which is toxic to yeast cells, is also toxic to human cells. We can consume alcohol due to alcohol dehydrogenase, an enzyme produced by humans and many other animals that catalyzes the oxidation of alcohols to aldehydes. In this reaction, nicotinamide adenine dinucleotide (NAD^+) is used as an oxidizing agent.

$$CH_3CH_2OH + NAD^+ \xrightarrow{\text{alcohol dehydrogenase}} CH_3CHO + NADH + H^+$$

ethanol   acetaldehyde

Not only does alcohol dehydrogenase allow humans to detoxify (within limits!) the ethanol that we consume, it also detoxifies the alcohol produced by certain fermentative microbes that reside in our small intestine and colon.

1. Draw molecules of ethanol and acetaldehyde.

   Student sketches should appear as follows:

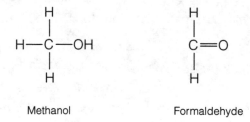

2. Explain why ethanol is considered an electron donor in this redox reaction.

   Ethanol loses electrons when it is converted to acetaldehyde. The carbon atom in ethanol that is bonded to the hydroxyl group is the same as the carbon atom in acetaldehyde that is double-bonded to oxygen.

3. Consumption of methanol can be fatal because alcohol dehydrogenase converts methanol to formaldehyde, a highly toxic substance that can cause the death of cells in the human body. Formaldehyde is the substance once commonly used to preserve animal and plant tissues; however, due to its cancer-causing properties, its use is restricted. Draw molecules of methanol and formaldehyde.

   Student sketches should appear as follows:

   $$\underset{\text{Methanol}}{\overset{\displaystyle H}{\underset{\displaystyle H}{H-C-OH}}} \qquad \underset{\text{Formaldehyde}}{\overset{\displaystyle H}{\underset{\displaystyle H}{C=O}}}$$

4. What is oxidized and reduced in this reaction? Explain.

$$CH_3OH + NAD^+ \xrightarrow{\text{alcohol dehydrogenase}} CH_2O + NADH + H^+$$

   methanol   formaldehyde

   Methanol is oxidized and NAD$^+$ is reduced.

5. Treatment for methanol ingestion involves giving the patient an alcohol dehydrogenase inhibitor. Explain why this is helpful.

   The conversion of methanol to formaldehyde is prevented because the enzyme necessary to catalyze the reaction is not available.

   (Note: The methanol eventually is excreted via the urinary system.)

6. During fermentation in yeast, alcohol dehydrogenase catalyzes a reaction that breaks down acetaldehyde into ethanol and regenerates NAD^+. Note that this is the reverse of the reaction catalyzed by the enzyme in humans and other animals.

alcohol dehydrogenase

$$CH_3CHO + NADH + H^+ \longrightarrow CH_3CH_2OH + NAD^+$$

acetaldehyde   ethanol

   a. What is oxidized and reduced in this reaction? Explain.

      NADH is oxidized to NAD^1. Acetaldehyde is reduced to ethanol.

   b. What happens to the ethanol after it is produced?

      The toxic alcohol is rapidly transported from the yeast cell to the external environment.

   c. What happens to the NAD^+ after it is produced?

      This oxidizing agent is used in other redox reactions within the cell.

Additional Investigation

IV. More Human Uses of Fermentation

Things are fermenting everywhere! Choose a product from the list below. Use your text and other resources, including primary sources, to find out how fermentation is used to make this product. Write a paper of 1–3 pages, based on reliable sources, indicating:

- the organism(s) doing the fermenting
- the metabolic pathway(s) used
- substrates
- fermentation products
- how the fermentation is accomplished
- how the product is prepared for consumption

Products

Sausage	Tempeh	Dental caries (product is the
Chocolate	Kimchee	decayed tooth)
Coffee	Sauerkraut	Vinegar
Sourdough bread	Citric acid (widely used as an	Yogurt
Cheeses	ingredient)	

Students, working individually or in groups, should submit a paper of 1–3 pages on how fermentation is involved in the production of one of the products listed in the student version. The paper should be based on reliable sources. Consider asking students for at least one primary literature article. The paper should address the following items:

- *the organism doing the fermenting*
- *the metabolic pathway(s) used*
- *substrates*
- *fermentation products*
- *how the fermentation is accomplished*
- *how the product is prepared for consumption*

As an alternative to a paper, you could ask students to create a poster.

V. Open-Ended Investigations

Use the working wine model (available at http://bioquest.org/icbl/casebook/wine) to conduct your own investigations of factors involved in wine fermentation.

Additional pairs of graphs (A and B or C and D) are available on the same website for further practice in interpreting graphs, making inferences, and drawing conclusions.

References

Noda, F., K. Hayashi, and T. Mizunuma. Antagonism between osmophilic lactic acid bacteria and yeasts in brine fermentation of soy sauce. *Applied and Environmental Microbiology,* 40(3):4452–457, 1980.

Stanley, Ethel D., Howard T. Odum, Elisabeth C. Odum, and Virginia G. Vaughan. Modeling wine fermentation, pp. 85–92, and software on CD-ROM. In J. R. Jungck, M. F. Fass, and E. D. Stanley, *Microbes Count!* Beloit, WI: BioQUEST Curriculum Consortium and American Society for Microbiology Press, 2003.

Chapter 3:

The Donor's Dilemma

INSTRUCTOR'S GUIDE

As with all the cases in this book, please read the preface if you have not already done so. In the preface you will find suggestions for using Investigative Case–Based Learning (ICBL) in different instructional situations such as starting a new lecture topic, assessing what students already know, setting a context for lab activities, and so on. The preface also describes ways to use cases in a variety of classroom settings and suggests multiple ways to assess learning with cases.

The Donor's Dilemma accompanies Unit Three: Genetics in Campbell and Reece's *Biology*, 8th edition. The case, which is about the West Nile virus, emphasizes material in Chapter 17: From Gene to Protein, Chapter 19: Viruses, and Chapter 20: Biotechnology. Students are provided with cues to refer to a few other selected sections in Unit 3. Students begin this investigative case by reading a narrative about a young man who, while donating blood, expresses a fear that he may have come in contact with West Nile virus. There are five strands in the case:

- WNV transmission

- Mutations in WNV

- The life cycles of WNV and HIV

- Using RT-PCR to test for WNV in blood donations

- Using genomics to track the spread of WNV in the United States (addressed in the Additional Investigation)

Students should complete the Case Analysis immediately following the reading of the case. We strongly suggest that students work in groups to complete the Case Analysis. Actively listening to and challenging the ideas of others can help learners become aware of their own misconceptions, yet also value their own and others' prior knowledge.

Six investigations accompany *The Donor's Dilemma*. Four are "core" investigations relating directly to the facts of the case, two are additional investigations that extend the case to another application, and one is an open-ended investigation. Table IG3.1 describes what students will gain from each investigation.

Table IG3.1 The Donor's Dilemma Case Overview.

Investigation	Learning Goals	Inquiry Skills Used
Core Investigations		
I. Transmission of WNV	Students read about the various ways that WNV can be transmitted. They learn vocabulary words such as titer, reservoir host, and incidental host. Then they relate various scenarios to a model of the transmission cycle.	• analysis and application of transmission cycle to the person in the case
II. Critical Reading	Students use Chapter 17 and Chapter 19 for information to identify, categorize, and determine the consequences of mutations in WNV. They gain practice in translating RNA codons.	• manual methods of analyzing aligned gene sequences • making predictions • making inferences • mathematical analysis of changes in sequence • classification of mutations
III. West Nile Virus: Viral Structure and Life Cycle	Students compare the WNV life cycle to a diagram of the HIV life cycle in the text. They learn more about the viral variations from gene to protein.	• classification of viruses • applications of visual information
IV. Testing Blood Donations for WNV	The RT-PCR test used to detect WNV in blood is introduced. Students identify the target cDNA for which the primer is specific.	• applying understanding of DNA replication to PCR test for WNV
Additional Investigation		
V. Tracking WNV	Students analyze a "box shade" presentation of aligned WNV sequences. Students analyze the differences in these data and propose explanations of likely sources of WNV in the United States.	• critical analysis of maps and other tools as visual data sets
VI. Open-Ended Investigations	Students can access the West Nile Virus Problem Space to gain access to data sets, online tools, and methlogies for investigating their own questions about the spread and evolution of WNV.	• posing questions • working with sophisticated genomics and protcomics tools • designing meaningful investigations • working with complex, large data sets

Table IG3.2 contains several resources related to *Biology*, 8th edition, that will help your students further their understanding of this case. Note that chapter readings and activities are listed in order of importance in regard to the case.

Table IG3.2 Campbell-Related Resources.

Resource	Chapter/Activity	Topics Covered/Activity Titles
Critical Reading from *Biology*, 8th edition	Chapter 17: From Gene to Protein	Protein synthesis (Concepts 17.1–17.4); point mutations (Concept 17.7)
	Chapter 19: Viruses	Viral reproduction (Concept 19.1); viruses as pathogens in animals (Concept 8.2)
Related Readings	Chapter 20: Biotechnology	PCR (Concept 20.5)
Campbell website/ CD-ROM	Chapter 17 **Activities**	Overview of Protein Synthesis, Translation
	Chapter 19 **Activity**	Retrovirus (HIV) Reproductive Cycle

Case Narrative

Students were asked to underline terms or phrases in the introductory narrative that they think are important to understanding the case. Suggested terms and phrases that students might have chosen are in bold type.

Usually, Russell found an excuse not to participate in company-sponsored blood drives, but for the first time he decided to donate blood. After filling out the **donor eligibility** form and passing the blood pressure, pulse, temperature, and blood-clotting tests, Russell sat down for his interview.

Russell interrupted the long list of "Have you ever?" questions with a question of his own. "What if I have **West Nile virus**?"

"West Nile virus is **uncommon**," the interviewer said. "Besides, **all donated blood is tested** for West Nile virus, even here in **California where it's extremely rare**." She glanced over his paperwork. "Let's see. You said you **haven't had any fevers** or headaches in the **last week**.

Is there a reason that you think you might have it?"

"No, but I've heard that sometimes **people don't have any symptoms**," Russell responded. "**I just got back** from **a hiking trip in Boulder, Colorado,** over the Fourth of July weekend. There were news reports that there are **a lot of cases** of the virus there, and I'm still covered with **mosquito bites**."

"Well, if you have West Nile virus, we will find out. Lab tests on your blood will identify the **presence of genetic material from the virus**," the interviewer said reassuringly. "WNV can only be transmitted through blood transfusions if there are virus particles in the donated blood. In the U.S., **only a tiny fraction of blood donations** last year tested positive for West Nile virus."

"So if I have West Nile virus, **could you tell if I got it in Colorado?**" Russell asked.

"Well, they **can't tell from this blood screening**, but **other tests can identify the strain** of WNV," she replied. "When West Nile virus **first**

appeared in New York in 1999, all the samples were alike. But now **mutations are showing up in the virus as it migrates to different areas.** We're seeing strains of the virus in different regions of the country."

"So did West Nile virus originate in New York?" Russell wondered.

"No," she said with a smile, **"it's called *West Nile* for a reason."**

Suggested Answers for Case Analysis

1. **Recognize potential issues and major topics in the case.** What is this case about? Underline terms or phrases that seem to be important to understanding this case. Then list **3–4** biology-related topics or issues in the case.

   Biology-related topics or issues: protecting the blood supply, detecting diseases in blood, patients' concerns for their health, how WNV is transmitted, how one is tested for WNV, spread of WNV, mutations.

2. **What specific questions do you have about these topics?** By yourself, or better yet, in a group, make a list of what you already know about this case in the "What Do I Know?" column. List questions you would like to learn more about in the "What Do I Need to Know?" column.

   There are many possible answers, depending on the experience of your students. Following are some likely responses:

What Do I Know?	What Do I Need to Know?
• *Viruses cause fevers.*	• *Does Russell have it?*
• *There are no cures for viruses.*	• *How does the blood test work?*
• *Vaccines are used to prevent viral infections.*	• *How does WNV reproduce and spread?*
• *WNV is related to bird flu.*	• *How long will it take to find out if you have WNV when you give blood?*
• *The blood supply is tested for HIV and WNV.*	• *Where is West Nile?*
• *Genetic material is nucleic acid.*	• *How did the virus get to the United States?*
• *DNA is genetic material.*	

3. Put a check mark by **1–3** questions or issues in the "What Do I Need to Know?" list that you think are most important to explore.

   Most students will use the contextual clues of being in a biology class and beginning the genetics unit to identify questions about the genetics of viruses.

4. **What kinds of references or resources would help you answer or explore these questions?** Identify two different resources and explain what information each resource is likely to give that will help you answer the question(s). Choose specific resources.

   You should expect a range of responses. Accept any reasonable resource (e.g., text, other book, Internet sites, maps, data tables, and so on) that could be related to the case. The answer "the Web" is too vague. Students should explain the type of site they are looking for or search terms they might use.

Suggested Answers for Core Investigations

I. Transmission of West Nile Virus (WNV)

West Nile virus is an arbovirus (**ar**thropod **bo**rne) that infects birds, humans, and other animals. Although the virus was first detected in Uganda in 1937, the first bird and human cases of West Nile virus in the United States were reported in New York City in 1999. Since then, it has spread throughout much of North America. Mosquitoes are the vectors for the virus, transmitting it to the animals that they feed upon. Although mosquitoes feed on many types of vertebrates, birds are the most likely source of the virus. The virus multiplies at a very fast rate in the blood of many bird species, producing a high viral titer (concentration of virus particles in blood). Many bird species are known as *reservoir hosts* for the virus because they can "store" a high concentration of virus particles in their blood. When a mosquito feeds on the blood of a reservoir host, it will likely take in enough virus particles to transmit the virus to another potential host (Figure 3.2).

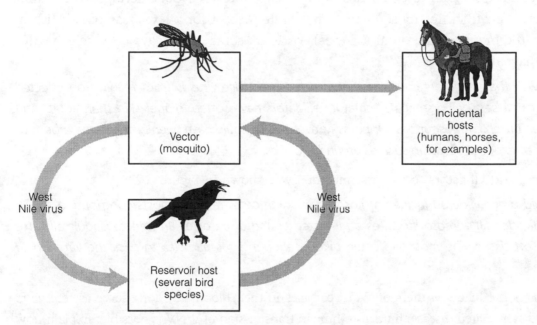

Figure 3.2 West Nile virus transmission cycle.

The interactions between infected birds and mosquitoes can quickly increase the incidence of WNV in a particular location, resulting in a cycle of viral amplification. The more mosquitoes there are, the more the virus is spread. The more birds that are present to be infected, the greater the number of virus particles that will be available to more mosquitoes.

Other animals, including humans, often serve as *incidental hosts*. Within incidental hosts, WNV is less efficient at multiplying; therefore, the concentration of the virus in the blood of these animals during infection is too low for mosquito vectors to pick up and transmit WNV to another host. Typically, these animals do not contribute to the cycle of amplification. West Nile virus can also be transmitted when an organism eats an infected organism. For example, crows that feed on the decaying flesh of other birds may contract West Nile virus through bird-to-bird transmission.

Eighty percent of humans who are infected with WNV show no symptoms. Twenty percent of those infected may experience fever, headache, fatigue, and body aches. Of the 20% with symptoms, only about 1 person in 150 develops encephalitis, a serious swelling of the brain that can cause death. In cases of WNV, viremia—presence of virus in the blood—lasts approximately 6 days or less. The amount of genetic material produced from the virus (a measure of viral titer) averages less than 5,000 copies of the virus per mL of blood. By comparison, other forms of viral encephalitis can result in a titer of 25,000,000 copies per mL of blood.

Human-to-human transmission of WNV through blood and organ donation, as well as during pregnancy or nursing, has been reported. Screening tests, including nucleic acid amplification and antibody detection, have been developed for WNV. (You will learn more about nucleic acid amplification in Investigation II.) Antibody detection tests are not used for screening blood because by the time the immune system produces antibodies in detectable amounts, the majority of the virus particles have been destroyed.

1. Several alligator farms in the southeastern United States reported an unusually high number of alligator deaths between 2001 and 2003. WNV was determined to be responsible for many of these deaths. Blood samples from infected alligators revealed high titers (some of which were higher than the titers in reservoir host bird species) for WNV. Considering that an adult alligator's hide is too thick for mosquitoes to penetrate (except for a few areas of soft tissue, such as inside the mouth and around the eyes), what are some other ways in which the alligators might have acquired WNV?

   One possible way that alligators could have contracted West Nile virus is from feeding on infected birds, chicken carcasses, or horsemeat. Immature alligators have softer, thinner skin than adults and could have been bitten by mosquitoes. Or possibly, even adults could have been bitten in the mouth or on other areas of exposed soft skin such as around the eyes.

2. How would you add alligators to the transmission cycle shown in Figure 3.2?

   Alligators would be considered incidental hosts or in some cases reservoir hosts contributing to the cycle of amplification. If a mosquito bites an infected young alligator or an infected adult alligator in an area of soft tissue, the mosquito could take in enough virus particles to pass the virus on to another host.

3. Although humans produce low titers of WNV particles in their blood and don't serve as reservoirs for this vector-disseminated disease, human-to-human transmission of WNV is possible. Explain how a transfusion of infected blood can result in the dissemination of WNV.

   In order for West Nile virus to be spread from human to human through a blood transfusion, the donor must have been exposed to the virus recently and be viremic. Because such a large volume of blood is transferred from donor to recipient during a transfusion, there would be sufficient copies of the virus in the donated blood to initiate viremia in the recipient.

II. Critical Reading

Before delving further into this investigative case, you first should read Concepts 17.1, 17.2, and 17.4; "Types of Point Mutations" in Concept 17.5; and Concepts 19.1 and 19.3. You might also want to do two Chapter 17 Activities on the Campbell website (http://www.masteringbio.com) or CD-ROM—*Overview of Protein Synthesis* and *Translation*.

In "The Donor's Dilemma," Russell wondered if it would be possible to tell where someone contracted West Nile virus. This is indeed possible. West Nile virus is an RNA virus. Like other RNA viruses, it has a high mutation rate; therefore, the nucleic acid sequence of a virus strain in New York could be quite different from a virus strain found in Egypt, for example. Many strains of WNV have been identified, and information about their nucleic acid sequences are stored in publicly available databases such as GenBank.

The sequences found in these databases are actually DNA sequences. In a laboratory, it is possible to create a DNA version of an RNA genome by using enzymes called reverse transcriptases. The newly constructed DNA sequence can be compared quickly to the sequences stored in databases by using powerful software to perform the comparisons. In the following activity, you will manually compare a short sequence of DNA (50 nucleotides out of 11,000) from six samples of WNV collected in Africa and Europe (Table 3.2). This particular sequence is part of the gene that codes for a portion of the virus's envelope protein (*E* gene).

1. Before you begin your analysis of the nucleotide sequences, use the data in Table 3.1 to make a prediction about the sequence that you would expect to be most similar to the one from Egypt. Make a second prediction about the one you would expect to be most dissimilar. Include number, country, and year.

Table 3.1 Identification of DNA Samples for a Portion of the Envelope (*E*) Gene of WNV. (Berthet et al., 1997)

No.	Country	Year
1	Egypt	1951
2	France	1965
3	Senegal	1979
4	Senegal	1990
5	Uganda	?*
6	Madagascar	1986

*The specific year in which this sample was gathered in Uganda is unknown; however, it was after 1951.

Most similar: *#2, France, 1965*
Reason: *Closest in time, although not close geographically.*

Most dissimilar: *#4, Senegal, 1990*
Reason: *Furthest in time, even though fairly close geographically.*

Other answers should be accepted if the reasoning is legitimate.

2. To analyze the sequences in Table 3.2 (see the next page), you will use manual methods that were used by geneticists until the development of computer-based methods. However, to make your comparison easier, a software program has been used to align the sequences in the table. The basic technique for comparing sequences has three steps:

Examining the sequences for noticeable differences in length

Comparing the sequences nucleotide by nucleotide

Translating the sequences from codon to amino acid

a. Consider Sequence 1, the oldest sequence from the West Nile region of Egypt, to be the standard for comparison. Examine the sequences shown in Table 3.2 for noticeable differences in length. Gaps in sequences are sometimes inserted by the computer as it aligns the rest of the sequence.

These gaps are not present in the actual nucleic acid; however, they show up in the computer's output and often indicate certain kinds of mutations. Which of the sequences has either a deletion (gaps leading to a shorter length) or an insertion (leading to longer length)? Which type of mutation is it? Indicate by column number the affected nucleotides.

A deletion occurred in Sequence 3, columns 26–37.

Table 3.2 Alignment of Six Sequences of Part of a WNV Gene for Envelope Protein (see "Note" in References).

```
      1          10          20          30          40          50
1   CCAACCACTGTGGAGTCGCATGGAAACTACTCCACACAGATTGGGGCCAC

2   CCAACCACTGTGGAGTCGCATGGAAACTACTCCACACAGATTGGGGCCAC

3   CCGACGACCGTTGAATCTCATGGCA                AGATAGGGGCCAC

4   CCAACCACTGTGGAGTCGCATGGAAACTACCCCACACAGATTGGGGCCAC

5   CCAACGACCGTTGAATCTCATGGCAGTTATTCAGCACAGATAGGGGCCAC

6   CCGACGACTGTTGAATCTCATGGCAATTATTCAACACAGGTTGGGGCCAC
```

(Note that published DNA sequences, such as those shown here, are always the nontemplate strand of DNA; thus, it is directly comparable to mRNA. By replacing the T's with U's, these sequences can be directly translated using Figure 17.5 in your text. These are only fragments of the *E* gene sequence shown with the 5′ end to the left. The WNV genome is an open reading frame that starts before these first 50 nucleotides of the *E* gene.)

b. Next, analyze the differences in the columns of nucleotides to identify point mutations. Use a straightedge to keep your place, a highlighter, and a pen. Examine each vertical column in Table 3.2 starting at the left to look for variations from Sequence 1. If the nucleotides in a column match those of the standard sequence, highlight them. If there are deviations from the standard, circle them with the pen. For example, the first column contains all C's, so the whole column should be highlighted. The third column has two G's, which vary from the A in Sequence 1. The two G's would be circled in pen and all the A's highlighted. How many total point mutations did you identify?

31 total point mutations. (Note: The deletion in Sequence 3 is not a point mutation because it involves more than one base pair in a gene.)

c. Determine the percentage of point mutations in sequences 2 through 6 (number of point mutations/number of nucleotides in sample × 100%). Sequence 2 is done for you as an example. (*Note:* For Sequence 3, count only the nucleotides present in the sequence.)

Sequence 2 = (0/50) × 100% = 0%

Sequence 3 =

Sequence 4 =

Sequence 5 =

Sequence 6 =

Which sample shows the greatest difference in nucleotides from Sequence 1? Explain. (*Note: The 12 missing nucleotides in Sequence 3 should be considered as one deletion mutation rather than 12 point mutations because this deletion most likely occurred as one event.*)

Sequence 2: (0/50) × 100% = 0%; Sequence 3: (8/38) × 100% = 21%; Sequence 4: (1/50) × 100% = 2%; Sequence 5: (12/50) × 100% = 24%; Sequence 6: (10/50) × 100% = 20%.

Sequence 5, from Uganda, year of collection unknown, is the most different without changing the overall length of the sequence. However, Sequence 3, collected in Senegal in 1979, is the most changed. It has only 38 nucleotides, and within that, 8 substitutions. The 12 missing nucleotides count as 1 deletion mutation. Note: Mutations can also result in a strain that is more like the standard; however, here we are simply asking students to look for differences in sequences.

d. In the third and final step in comparing sequences, you need to translate each of the 6 sequences from codon to amino acid, using Figure 17.5 in your textbook. Then you will be able to observe the consequences of the different mutations on the resulting polypeptides. Normally, you would expect to see a start codon (AUG), but assume instead that the reading frame begins with the first nucleotide at the 5′ end. Write in the appropriate amino acids under the DNA sequences in Table 3.2.

Amino acids in boldface type are different from the standard.

Sequence 1: Pro-Thr-Thr-Val-Glu-Ser-His-Gly-Asn-Tyr-Ser-Thr-Gln-Ile-Gly-Ala

Sequence 2: Pro-Thr-Thr-Val-Glu-Ser-His-Gly-Asn-Tyr-Ser-Thr-Gln-Ile-Gly-Ala

Sequence 3: Pro-Thr-Thr-Val-Glu-Ser-His-Gly- **Lys**-*Ile-Gly-Ala*

*Sequence 4: Pro-Thr-Thr-Val-Glu-Ser-His-Gly-Asn-Tyr-***Pro***-Thr-Gln-Ile-Gly-Ala*

*Sequence 5: Pro-Thr-Thr-Val-Glu-Ser-His-Gly-***Ser***-Tyr-Ser-***Ala***-Gln-Ile-Gly-Ala*

*Sequence 6: Pro-Thr-Thr-Val-Glu-Ser-His-Gly-Asn-Tyr-Ser-Thr-Gln-***Val***-Gly-Ala*

e. Examine each sequence. How many amino acids differed from the standard in sequences 2 through 6? Which amino acids changed?

Sequence 2:

Sequence 3:

Sequence 4:

Sequence 5:

Sequence 6:

What does this information reveal about the effects of the mutations on the *E* gene and the protein it codes for?

Sequence 2: No mutations, no change in sequence

Sequence 3: There were five changes in amino acid sequence. The codons for four amino acids were lost in the deletion. Amino acid #13 is Lys in Sequence 3, but it is Gln in Sequence 1. (A protein can still function with some missing amino acids as long as the key amino acids are still in place. Four amino acids are missing due to the deletion, but in this case the protein is still functional.)

Sequence 4: One change. Amino acid #11 is Pro, instead of Ser.

Sequence 5: Two changes. Amino acid #9 is Ser, instead of Asn. Amino acid #12 is Ala, instead of Thr.

Sequence 6: One change. Amino acid #14 is Val, instead of Ile.

The effect of these mutations on the E gene is that the polypeptides, built-in response to this gene will have a primary structure that differs from the polypeptides in the standard sequence.

f. How many point mutations were involved in the amino acid differences you found? In Table 3.2, draw an asterisk by those nucleotides that made these differences.

Four point mutations made the difference. Students should have placed an asterisk above nucleotide 30 in Sequence 4; above nucleotides 26 and 34 in Sequence 5; and above nucleotide 40 in Sequence 6.

g. How many of the point mutations were nonsense mutations? How many were silent mutations?

Zero nonsense, 27 silent

h. Compare your answers in 2c to those in 2f. Is the percentage of point mutations related to how many amino acids are changed? Explain your response.

Percent point mutations does not tell you exactly how many amino acid substitutions will occur, but it might indicate trends (i.e., the more point mutations, the higher the likelihood of amino acid substitutions). Due to the redundancy of the genetic code, several different codon sequences code for the same amino acid.

i. Is it likely that the deletion mutation is also a frameshift mutation? Explain.

No. In order for the deletion in Sequence 3 to be a frameshift mutation, all of the nucleotides that are downstream of the deletion would be improperly grouped into codons, resulting in missense and, eventually, nonsense. This type of change does not occur in Sequence 3. The last two amino acids coded for (Gly and Ala) are the same as in Sequence 1; therefore, the downstream codons are not affected.

j. Now that you have identified, categorized, and determined the consequences of the various mutations in these sequences of WNV, how do these results compare to your predictions in question 1?

Answers will vary based on student predictions. A good answer, however, would relate the predictions to new conclusions based on sequence analyses. Students should take into account the total number of mutations in the different sequences as well as the effects of these mutations on the resulting amino acids. Relating their answers to geographic location might also be included.

III. West Nile Virus: Viral Structure and Life Cycle

West Nile virus is a relatively small, spherical virus whose genome is single-stranded RNA (ssRNA), which also serves as the messenger RNA (mRNA) coding for viral proteins (Figure 3.3). This genetic material is contained within an inner protein coat called a capsid. Like many other animal viruses, WNV also has a membranous envelope derived from the host cell. This membrane surrounds the capsid and has numerous glycoproteins (the E protein) encoded by the viral genome. These glycoproteins are located on the outer surface of the envelope and function in the recognition of potential host cells. You analyzed the sequence of a portion of this viral envelope glycoprotein gene in Investigation II.

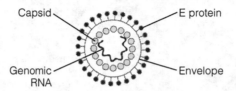

Capsid
E protein
Genomic RNA
Envelope

Figure 3.3 West Nile virus structure.

1. Animal viruses are classified by the type of nucleic acid found within the capsid. Using Table 19.1 in your textbook and the clues provided in the passage above, identify the classes for WNV and HIV. Provide an example of another virus from the same class for each.

   WNV Class _____   HIV Class _____

   Example: Example:

   WNV Class: IV
   Example: Yellow fever virus, rubella, common cold, polio

   HIV Class: VI
   Example: RNA tumor viruses, such as leukemia

2. Compare the structure of WNV to that of HIV (see Figure 19.8 in your text).
   Both viruses have envelopes that include glycoproteins. Each has a capsid with ssRNA inside.

3. How do the RNA molecules of these two viruses differ in number and function? In your response, consider the role of both in the formation of mRNA.
   WNV has one single-stranded RNA that can serve as mRNA. HIV has two single-stranded RNA molecules, either of which can be a template for the first strand of DNA synthesis using reverse transcriptase. This enzyme uses the first strand as a template to produce the second strand. These strands act as a template for double-stranded DNA synthesis.

4. Compare and contrast the reproductive life cycle of WNV (Figure 3.4) to that of HIV (see Figure 19.8 in your text).

Both viruses enter the cell after the interaction of envelope glycoproteins with the host plasma membrane. Both viruses contain ssRNA. WNV genomic RNA serves as mRNA upon entry of the virus into the

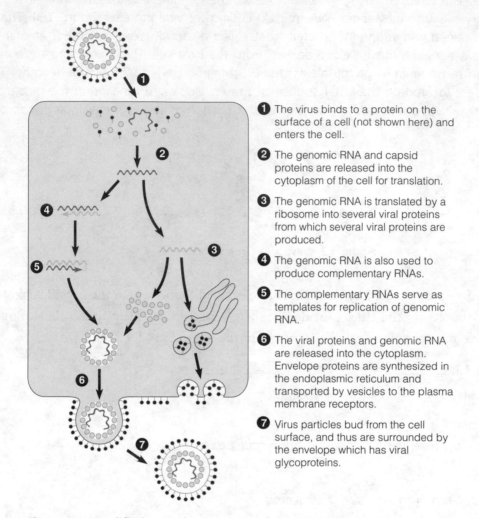

1 The virus binds to a protein on the surface of a cell (not shown here) and enters the cell.

2 The genomic RNA and capsid proteins are released into the cytoplasm of the cell for translation.

3 The genomic RNA is translated by a ribosome into several viral proteins from which several viral proteins are produced.

4 The genomic RNA is also used to produce complementary RNAs.

5 The complementary RNAs serve as templates for replication of genomic RNA.

6 The viral proteins and genomic RNA are released into the cytoplasm. Envelope proteins are synthesized in the endoplasmic reticulum and transported by vesicles to the plasma membrane receptors.

7 Virus particles bud from the cell surface, and thus are surrounded by the envelope which has viral glycoproteins.

Figure 3.4 Simplified reproductive cycle of the West Nile virus.

cell. In the host cell's cytoplasm, WNV transcribes a complementary strand of RNA to act as a template for producing more genomic RNA strands. HIV ssRNA is reverse transcribed, producing DNA that is complementary to the viral RNA. A second DNA strand is catalyzed, and the double-stranded DNA is incorporated into the host cell's DNA as a provirus. The life cycle of WNV does not involve the nucleus of the host cell.

5. Many viruses, including WNV, cold viruses, and flu viruses, reproduce in the host for a short period of time before being destroyed by the host's immune system. This production of new virus particles occurs during a period in which virus particles are present in the blood (viremia). If Russell, the blood donor in the case, had been infected with WNV, he could safely make future donations once the viremia had passed and his blood no longer contained virus particles. In contrast, a person infected with HIV can never give blood. Examine the life cycle of HIV and suggest a reason for this. (*Note:* An immune system response is usually initiated by recognition of "nonself" molecules on the surface of infected cells.)

When a person is infected with HIV, host cells retain the provirus in their own genome. The immune system cannot detect the HIV provirus within a host cell, and therefore, the provirus cannot be eradicated from the body. At any time, these provirus genes can produce mRNA that results in the formation of new HIV particles and their release into body fluids.

IV. Testing Blood Donations for WNV

To prevent human blood-to-blood transmission of WNV, all blood donations since June 2003 have been tested for the presence of WNV particles. The test used is called reverse transcription–polymerase chain reaction (RT-PCR).

A PCR cannot be run without DNA. Because WNV does not contain DNA, its RNA must be isolated and reverse transcribed (RT) to form complementary DNA (cDNA). (See Figure 20.8 for more information on PCR and Concept 20.4 for more information on RT-PCR.) When donor blood is tested for WNV, RNA is extracted from the blood sample. Individuals who are in the viremic phase of WNV will have West Nile virus RNA present in their blood, as well as other types of RNA, including their own. The mixed sample of "unknown" RNAs is reverse transcribed to create a mixed sample of cDNAs.

PCR utilizes polymerase enzymes and specific DNA "primers" to amplify (make many copies of) a targeted DNA sequence. Primers are short, single-stranded DNA molecules that match up to the two ends of the targeted DNA sequence and are necessary for the initiation of DNA synthesis. The DNA that matches up to the primers is then repeatedly duplicated in cycles of PCR, until it reaches detectable levels.

Primers specific for WNV cDNA are used in the PCR test referred to in this case. If WNV is present in the blood sample, then the cDNA will be amplified successfully. The primers ensure that a fragment will be amplified from this cDNA only. (For more information, see Khanna et al., cited in the references at the end of this investigative case.)

1. Why are primers needed for initiation of DNA synthesis using PCR? How do PCR primers differ from the primers in cells? (Hint: See Figure 16.16.)

   Primers are needed for PCR because DNA polymerases can add nucleotides only to preexisting strands of nucleic acids. In cells, the preexisting strands (primers) are RNA. In PCR, synthetic single-stranded DNA is used as a primer.

2. The following cDNA sequences (A–D) were obtained by reverse transcription of RNA samples from donated blood. One of the WNV primers used in RT-PCR has the following sequence:

   3' GGCTGCTGGCAACTT 5'

   Circle the cDNA sequence below that would be targeted by this WNV primer.

   A. 5' GGCTGCTGGCAACTT 3'

   B. 5' CCGACGACCGTTGAA 3'

   C. 5' TATAACCGTCCAAGTT 3'

   D. 5' CCGGCCTAGCATAGAA 3'

   B will be targeted. It has the complementary sequence to the primer, permitting hydrogen bonding.

3. Explain how primers control which cDNA is being amplified.

   Only those cDNAs that have sequences matching this primer and the other primers (not shown) would be WNV cDNA, the target of interest.

4. The day after Russell's blood sample was tested for WNV, he was told that the results were positive. What organisms were likely involved in Russell's infection with WNV? Is it likely he will pass on the disease?

Most likely, a mosquito that feeds on birds and mammals bit an infected bird and then bit Russell. As a human, Russell is an incidental host because it is unlikely that his titer will ever be high enough for him to be a reservoir host. If another mosquito bites him, the mosquito will not take in enough West Nile virus particles to infect other animals. Russell cannot transmit the disease to others unless his blood donation somehow becomes part of the blood supply.

Suggested Answers for Additional Investigations

V. Tracking West Nile Virus

A. Origin of the West Nile Virus in the United States. WNV was first isolated in Uganda in 1937 and has since spread throughout Africa and other parts of the world. As an emerging disease, WNV continues to generate both public and scientific interest. Researchers are exploring questions about its origin, evolution, transmission by multiple vectors and host tissues, replication in multiple hosts, detection, and vaccine potential. Central to these investigations are the use of molecular data, including nucleic acid sequences, and the use of bioinformatics (the application of computer science and mathematics to genetic and other biological information).

When WNV was first detected in New York City in 1999, researchers wanted to know where it came from and how it arrived. To propose an answer to these questions, using methods similar to those used in the analysis in Investigation II, you can look at similarities between a New York strain (NY99) of WNV isolated from a Bronx Zoo flamingo in 1999 and strains of WNV isolated from different parts of the world. (*Note:* In the following table, only a portion of the genomes were compared—specifically, a portion of the envelope protein gene. A software program called CLUSTALW was used to align the nucleic acid sequences found in these strains, and then a second program called BOXSHADE was used to display the sequences from the most similar to the least similar compared to the NY99 strain. The Case Book website provides links to instructions for using these programs.)

1. Scientists at the Centers for Disease Control and Prevention (CDC) concluded that NY99 most likely was transported to New York from Israel. Does the information in Table 3.3 support this

Table 3.3 BOXSHADE Plot of Aligned WNV *E* Gene Sequences from Various Strains

The BOXSHADE program automatically generates several colors to indicate properties of nucleic acids. To learn more, go to the Biology WorkBench website (see References).

conclusion? How many differences in sequence are there between the two samples? What other conclusion could you draw from comparing the NY99 and ISRAEL98 strains?

The ISRAEL98 strain is identical to NY99 for the sequences compared. Yes, Table 3.3 supports the conclusion that it is highly likely that the NY99 strain originated in Israel. One could also conclude that the NY99 strain did not come directly from Israel. Perhaps both strains originated from the same source.

2. Which strain is the most dissimilar to NY99? How many differences did you find between this strain and NY99? Do you find this result surprising? Explain.

MADAGASCAR88 has 15 differences in sequence. This is not too surprising considering that the strain was from 1988 and from a more remote geographic area.

3. How do you think WNV arrived in New York City? Consider what you've learned previously about transmission of this disease.

It is unlikely that a human traveler brought WNV to New York. We know that a human's viral titer is too low to enable mosquitoes to pick up the virus and transmit it to other organisms. The more likely hypothesis is that the virus came to New York by an infected bird, perhaps a migrating sea gull or a bird transported for agricultural or pet trade purposes. Mosquitoes feeding on birds can readily transmit WNV. Students may suggest that a mosquito came over on a boat or plane and served as the origin. Mosquitoes would not survive the boat trip. It is possible that an infected mosquito could have been transported on a plane, but the chance is a remote one when compared to the scenario of bird migration.

B. **Spread of WNV in the United States.** Since 1999, WNV has been carefully monitored. The CDC maintains resources including regional data and maps to track the spread of WNV in the United States. For example, the map in Figure 3.5 reflects both vector (mosquito) and host (birds, horses, humans, and so on) data collected by the CDC. Human cases reported in any state from 1999 through 2002 are distinguished by cross-hatching.

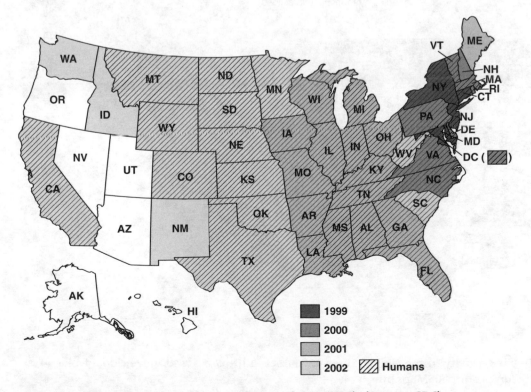

Figure 3.5 West Nile virus in the United States (1999–2002). (Source: CDC)

1. Construct a line graph that shows the number of states reporting the presence of WNV from 1999 through 2002.

   Students should have plotted the following information, with year on the x-axis and number of states reporting WNV on the y-axis.

2. Is proximity to known outbreaks of WNV a factor in its spread? Looking at the map in

Year	States Reporting WNV
1999	4
2000	12
2001	28
2002	44

   Figure 3.5, describe geographic factors that seem to influence the spread of WNV. Explain.

   The spread seems to be strongly related to geographic location. Over time, proximity to the source of the WNV seems to be the most important factor. Students might cite specific geographic examples, such as New York having the highest number of cases initially, then the Midwest having the most, then the far Plains states. The only anomaly is that cases in California are not contiguous with other states reporting WNV cases.

3. Examine the map in Figure 3.6 and compare it to that shown in Figure 3.5. In **3–4** sentences, describe the extent of spread in 2006.

   There are many appropriate answers to this question, and they may vary depending on what the stu-

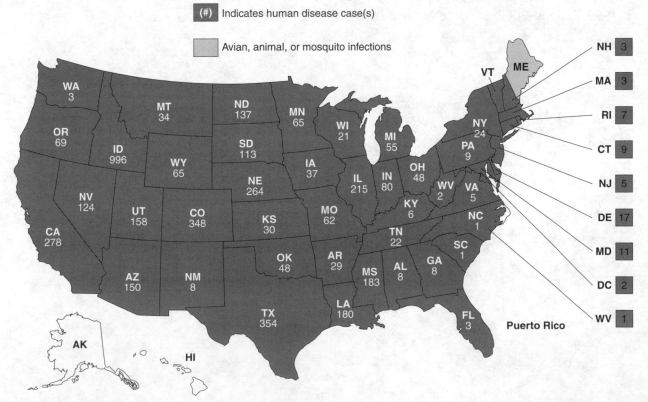

Figure 3.6 West Nile virus activity in the United States (2006), CDC: http://www.cdc.gov/ncidod/dvbid/westnile/Mapsactivity/surv&control/06Maps.htm

dents already know or what they may have looked up. Reasons might include more efficient vectors, increased population of reservoir hosts, more species of reservoir hosts, the establishment of public education about WNV, human lifestyles in Colorado versus those in New York, visitors and residents engaging in summer activities outdoors in Colorado, differences in climate and rainfall patterns, better eradication measures for vector populations in New York, and so on.

Consider differences in host and vector populations due to factors such as good breeding sites in the swamps versus those in the city. If birds congregate in large populations, transmission by vectors will increase. If mosquito vectors are able to access both birds and humans easily, transmission will increase. Consider differences in available mosquito species.

VI. Open-Ended Investigations

You may wish to visit the West Nile Virus Problem Space to use tools, methods, and data to explore the global spread and evolution of WNV.

The West Nile Virus Workbench Lab (Kiser, 2004) provides instruction on using the data and bioinformatics tools.

Additional Potential Investigations are listed in the WNV Problem Space at http://bioquest.org/bedrock/problem_space/wnv/curr_resources.php.

References

Berthet, F.-X., H. G. Zeller, M.-T. Drouet, J. Rauzier, J.-P. Digoutte, and V. Deubel. Extensive nucleotide changes and deletions within the envelope glycoprotein gene of Euro-African West Nile viruses. *Journal of General Virology*, 1997, vol. 78(9), pp. 2293–2297, 1997.

Note: Table 3.2 presents an alignment of published DNA sequences of WNV, edited for length. We obtained these sequences from GenBank using identifiers provided by Berthet et al. (see reference above). The sequence identifiers are: EGY-HEg101/51, FRA-PaH651/65, SEN-AnD27875/79, SEN-ArD78016/90, UGA-MP22/?, and MAD-ArMg956/86. We then used the nucleic acid alignment tool CLUSTALW on these sequences. The Biology Workbench was the interface that provided the nucleic acid tools and access to the San Diego Supercomputer. It may be freely accessed at http://workbench.sdsc.edu.

Khanna, M., K. J. Henrickson, K. Harrington, C. R. Waters, J. Meece, K. Reed, and S. Shukla. "Multiplex PCR–EHA Compared to 'Real Time' Taqman for the Surveillance and Diagnosis of West Nile Virus." Prodesse Inc., Waukesha, WI, Medical College of Wisconsin, Milwaukee, and Marshfield Clinic Research Foundation, Marshfield, Wis. Presented at the 11th International Conference on Infectious Diseases, March 2004, in Cancun, Mexico. http://www.prodesse.com/resources/ICID_2004_WNV.pdf

Kiser, Stacey. West Nile Virus Workbench Lab. 2004. http://bioquest.org/bedrock/problem_spaces/wnv/curr_resources.php (accessed July 2, 2007).

Chapter 4:

Tree Thinking

INSTRUCTOR'S GUIDE

As with all the cases in this book, please read the preface if you have not already done so. In the preface you will find suggestions for using Investigative Case–Based Learning (ICBL) in different instructional situations such as starting a new lecture topic, assessing what students already know, setting a context for lab activities, and so on. The preface also describes ways to use cases in a variety of classroom settings and suggests multiple ways to assess learning with cases.

Tree Thinking accompanies Unit Four: Mechanisms of Evolution in Campbell and Reece's *Biology*, 8th edition. The case emphasizes material covered in Chapter 26: Phylogeny and the Tree of Life and provides clues that will lead students to look at other chapters in this unit. There are five strands in the case:

- Preparing cladograms using observable characters

- Using bioinformatics and DNA testing as forensic methods to detect illegal whale products

- Comparing unknown sequences to a database of known cetacean sequences

- Comparing trees prepared using morphological and molecular characters

- Considering the biological impacts and ethics of whaling (addressed in the Additional Investigation)

Students should complete the Case Analysis immediately following the reading of the case. We strongly suggest that students work in groups to complete the Case Analysis. Actively listening to and challenging the ideas of others can help learners become aware of their own misconceptions, yet also value their own and others' prior knowledge.

Six investigations accompany *Tree Thinking*. Three are "core" investigations relating directly to the facts of the case, one is an additional investigation that extends the case to another application with a strong science-technology-society connection, and two provide opportunities for open-ended exploration. Table IG4.1 describes what students will gain from each investigation.

Table IG4.1 Tree Thinking Case Overview.

Investigation	Learning Goals	Inquiry Skills Used
Core Investigations		
I. Critical Reading	Using fictional plants, students interpret and develop morphologically based cladograms as hypotheses about relationships among the taxa.	• generating comparisons • interpreting data • working with conventions of cladistics
II. Whale Meat Forensics	Using the information from the Web tool "Witness for the Whales," students examine genetic similarity trees based on mitochondrial DNA sequences from various cetacean sources. They make inferences about the species identity of whale meat products.	• learning to use rooted trees produced with bioinformatics tools to identify unknowns • using online data tools
III. Which Mammals Are Most Closely Related to Whales?	The Whippo problem space is introduced. Students investigate phylogenetic trees as hypothetical explanations of evolutionary relationships among whales and their terrestrial relatives.	• inferring relationships from models
Additional Investigation		
IV. Position Paper on Whaling	Students explore the biological impacts and systematics of whaling and consider sustainable management of whale populations.	• identifying reliable resources of data • reasoning from data to prepare position papers about whaling based on many kinds of evidence
V. Open-Ended Investigations	A. Students use additional data to modify Dendro-grammaceac cladograms B. Using Biology Workbench, students find new sequences from other taxa to examine the relationships with the cetaceans.	• identifying characteristics from visual data • representing hypotheses as cladograms • using additional bioinformatics search tools to locate additional sequences • using alignment tools and tree drawing tools with these data

Table IG4.2 contains several resources related to *Biology*, 8th edition, that will help your students further their understanding of this case. Note that chapter readings and activities are listed in order of importance in regard to the case.

Table IG4.2 Campbell-Related Resources.

Resource	Chapter/Activity	Topics Covered/Activity Titles
Critical Reading from *Biology*, 8th edition	Chapter 26: Phylogeny and the Tree of Life	Concepts 26.1–26.3
Related Readings from *Biology*, 8th edition	Chapter 22: Descent with Modification: A Darwinian View of Life	Homology, Figure 22.17 and Figure 22.18; The Fossil Record, Figure 22.15 and Figure 22.16 (Concept 22.3)
	Chapter 34: Vertebrates	Exploring Mammalian Diversity, Figure 34.36
	Chapter 40: An Basic Principles of Animal From and Function	Evolutionary Convergence in Fast Swimmers (Fusiform Shape), Figure 40.2 (Concept 40.1)
Campbell website/CD-ROM	Chapter 22 **Activity**	Reconstructing Forelimbs
	Chapter 26 **Investigation**	How Is Phylogeny Determined by Comparing Proteins?

Case Narrative

Students were asked to underline terms or phrases in the introductory narrative that they think are important to understanding the case. Suggested terms and phrases that students might have chosen are in bold type.

Teruko and her friend Sean were jogging around a track after work. "So, Teruko, how was your brother's wedding in **Japan**?" Sean asked.

"It was amazing! I couldn't believe the ceremony," Teruko said. "The reception had some unusual food prepared by special chefs. My favorite was the **kujira**."

"What's kujira?" Sean asked.

"**It's whale meat**," Teruko replied. When Sean made a face, Teruko continued. "I know it sounds awful, but it tasted so good. In fact, my dad even tried to bring some canned whale meat back, but customs agents took it at the airport."

"Why?" Sean asked. "Isn't **whaling legal in Japan**?"

"Sort of. This happened at U.S. Customs. It turns out that you **can't bring in any product that is made from marine mammals because so many species are endangered**," Teruko explained.

"Oh, that makes sense," Sean said. "So, **did your dad get into trouble** at the airport?"

"No, they just took the cans away," Teruko sighed.

"I've heard there's a **huge black market for whale** meat in Asia, and some people pay the equivalent of **$400 a pound**," Sean added.

"Yes, and they even have biotech tests now to tell if the meat is really from whales."

"**How can they tell what type of meat** is in the can?" Sean asked.

"Well, **they extract DNA from the sample** and **compare its sequence to known DNA whale sequences**. In fact, **forensic DNA testing** of 'whale meat' from **Asian markets** has turned up **dolphin, shark, and even horse meat**."

"Hm. Maybe they should run the same tests on the meat we had at lunch yesterday," Sean laughed. Now it was Teruko's turn to make a face.

Suggested Answers for Case Analysis

1. **Recognize potential issues and major topics in the case.** What is this case about? Underline terms or phrases that seem to be important to understanding this case. Then list **3 or 4** biology-related topics or issues in the case.

   Biology-related topics or issues: using DNA to test foods, using DNA and biotechnology to identify species, whaling regulations, ethical issues

2. **What specific questions do you have about these topics?** By yourself, or better yet, in a group, make a list of what you already know about this case in the "What Do I Know?" column. List questions you would like to learn more about in the "What Do I Need to Know?" column.

   There are many possible answers, depending on the experiences of your students. Some likely responses follow.

What Do I Know?	What Do I Need to Know?
• Whales are mammals.	• When did whales become marine organisms?
• DNA is unique among species.	• What are the tests done on the DNA? How?
• DNA sequences can be identified and aligned (if they did Case 3 or have studied the genetics unit).	• What can researchers tell from the tests?
	• How are whale species identified?
• DNA is a good forensic tool for evaluating relatedness.	• What species of whales are endangered?
	• How many whales are there in the world?
• Those students who have traveled to Japan or Asia may have information to share.	• What methods do Japanese whalers use?
	• What are the regulations about whaling?
• Those students who have seen whales may have information to share.	• How does U.S. Customs work?
	• Why is this case called "Tree Thinking" when it's about whales?
• Whales communicate using sounds.	
• Some whales migrate long distances.	
• Whales are the largest animals that have lived on Earth.	

3. Put a check mark by **1–3** questions or issues from the "What Do I Need to Know?" list that you think are most important to explore.

   You should expect a range of responses. Most students will use the contextual clues of being in a biology class and beginning an evolution unit to identify systematics-related questions.

4. **What kinds of references or resources would help you answer or explore these questions?** Identify two different resources and explain what information each resource is likely to give that will help you answer the question(s). Choose specific resources.

Accept any reasonable resource (e.g., text, other book, Internet sites, maps, data tables, and so on) that could be related to this case. The answer "the Web" is too vague. Students should explain the type of site they are looking for or search terms they might use.

Suggested Answers for Core Investigations

I. Critical Reading

To complete this investigation, you should have already read Chapter 26: Phylogeny and the Tree of Life.

A. Morphological Observations: Identifying Characters in the Dendrogrammaceae. In this exercise, you will observe and record morphological characters and investigate the construction of a cladogram based on five characters.

Begin by reviewing Figure 4.2 and Table 4.1. Then record the presence or absence of the five characters that are examined in Table 4.1. A "0" indicates that a taxon does not exhibit the particular character. Enter a "1" if the taxon does exhibit a particular character. For example, taxa B, C, and D have narrow leaves, so a "1" has been entered in the table.

1. Which trait in Table 4.1 is shared by at least four taxa? Which taxa are they?

Character 2 (united petals, not separate) is shared by taxa A, B, C, and D.

2. All five characters are present in which taxon?

All five characters are present in taxon D.

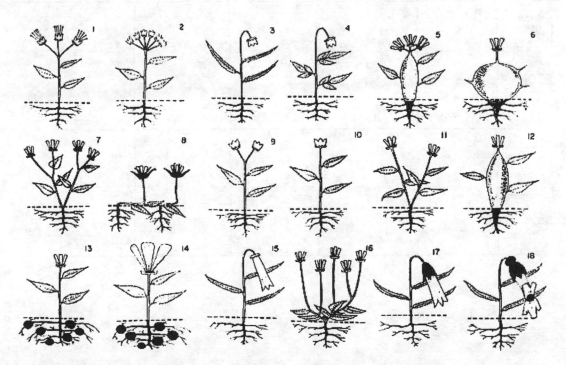

Figure 4.2 The Dendrogrammaceae, an imaginary family of flowering plants (Wagner, W. H., Jr., 2001).

Table 4.1 Observation and Identification of Morphological Characters.

(Refer to your text for definitions of unknown terms.)

Selected Taxa	1 Leaves Narrow	2 United Petals, Not Separate	3 Tubelike Petals	4 Elongated Sepals	5 Flower with Bilateral, Not Radial, Symmetry
A	0				
B	1				
C	1				
D	1				
E	0				

3. Are any of these characters shared by all five taxa?

No.

Table IG4.3 Answers to Student Table 4.1.

Selected Taxa	1 Leaves Narrow	2 United Petals, Not Separate	3 Tubelike Petals	4 Elongated Sepals	5 Flower with Bilateral, Not Radial, Symmetry
A	0	1	0	0	0
B	1	1	1	0	0
C	1	1	1	1	0
D	1	1	1	1	1
E	0	0	0	0	0

4. One methodology that has proven useful in developing cladograms is to include a taxon that is less related to the other taxa. This "outgroup" is assumed to have ancestral forms of the characters found in these taxa. Characters that are not shared with this "outgroup" taxon are considered derived. Which taxon is the outgroup in this plant family example?

Taxon E is the outgroup.

B. Examining a Cladogram. By constructing a cladogram using the morphological characters recorded in Table 4.1, you can infer relatedness among the taxa. Cladograms can be helpful depictions of patterns in levels of relatedness for shared characters among taxa. Taxa are sorted by presence or absence of characters. However, branch distances in a cladogram do not imply chronology. (Phylogenetic trees present hypotheses about the evolution of taxa and imply chronology in diverging branch points.)

Using the characters in Table 4.1, the following cladogram indicates the relationships among the five taxa selected from the Dendrogrammaceae. Notice that there are branches in Figure 4.3 associated with each taxon. Each node is called a clade. Branches C and D are nested within the larger clade that includes B.

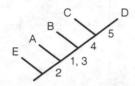

Figure 4.3 The characters are placed below the diagonal. The taxa A, B, C, D, and E are positioned in branches along the diagonal to indicate which characters they share.

1. Which character in Figure 4.3 is exclusively shared by taxa C and D?

   Character 4

2. Consider character 1 in the cladogram. Which taxa lack this character?

   Taxa E and A

3. Can you estimate how much time passed between the development of character 2 and character 4? Explain.

   No. Although character 4 could be more recently derived because it is shared by fewer taxa farther along the axis, cladograms do not imply chronology.

4. Compare the table of characters to the cladogram. Do cladograms contain the same information as the table? Are cladograms more useful? Explain.

   Cladograms allow you to group taxa by shared characters in a concise format. You can look at the relationships between taxa by reorganizing the table as a cladogram. Cladograms are useful for constructing a nested distribution of characters to think about related groups productively and generate hypotheses about relatedness.

C. Identifying Primitive Versus Derived Characters. Simple observation helps differentiate morphological characteristics of these plant taxa, but what characters can help us understand the evolutionary relationships between taxa? To be useful for cladistics, characters must be homologous (reflect shared ancestry). Among the homologous characters, we need to identify the following:

- Shared primitive characters: homologous traits that are common to larger taxonomic groups; for example, flowers are found in all angiosperms.

- Shared derived characters: homologous traits that are limited to particular taxa; for example, flowers with united petals are found in only some angiosperms.

Depending on the taxa included in a cladogram, the same character could be considered primitive in one cladogram and derived in another. For example, consider milk production of mammals. When the taxa are all mammals, then milk production is a primitive character. However, when the taxa include reptiles, birds, and mammals, then milk production is a derived character.

1. Look at the complete group of taxa in Figure 4.2. Select a taxon with a morphological character (other than those you used in Table 4.1) that you think is a shared derived character. What makes it likely to be derived?

   If the presence of a character enables you to differentiate between Dendrogrammaceae taxa, it is a shared derived character for those taxa with the character. A number of taxa could be selected. Some good choices would include derived characters such as multiple flowers (inflorescences such as 2, 9) or tubers (stems adapted for storage such as 13, 14) or other storage modifications (5, 6, 12).

D. Revising a Cladogram. Systematists use existing data or gather new data to consider carefully which characters to use in constructing a cladogram. Determination of the branch points is based on these characters. As new data are discovered, a cladogram may be reconstructed to incorporate the new information.

Figure 4.4 Sketch based on a new fossil of extinct Dendrogrammaceae, taxon F.

1. Enter your observations of taxon F in Table 4.2. *Note:* These are the same five characters used in Table 4.1.

Table 4.2 Character Table for Taxon F.

Selected Taxa	1 Leaves Narrow	2 United Petals, Not Separate	3 Tubelike Petals	4 Elongated Sepals	5 Flower with Bilateral, Not Radial, Symmetry
F					

Table IG4.4 Answers to Student Table 4.2.

Selected Taxa	1 Leaves Narrow	2 United Petals, Not Separate	3 Petals Tubelike, Much Longer Than Wide	4 Elongated Sepals	5 Flower with Bilateral, Not Radial, Symmetry
F 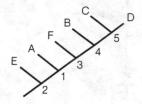	1	1	0	0	0

2. Use the character information from taxon F to redraw the cladogram (Figure 4.3).

```
                    C
              B        D
        F           5
      A          4
  E          3
        1
      2
```

II. "Whale Meat Forensics"

A. Using Biotechnology and Systematics. In this investigation you will be working with DNA sequence analysis. You should be familiar with the DNA analysis methods covered in Chapter 20.

People in many regions of the world rely on animals harvested from the sea as a significant source of protein. Several cultures enjoy traditional dishes made from whale meat (Figure 4.5). With declining populations of cetaceans (the mammalian order to which whales and their close relatives belong), however, this practice has come under international scrutiny.

From 1993 to 1999, researchers from New Zealand (Baker et al., 2000) analyzed genetic variations in a defined region of cetacean DNA. One of their goals was to identify food products containing meat from protected or endangered cetacean species or noncetacean sources. Investigators began by taking tissue samples from beached and harvested cetaceans. Species identifications of the animals were done onsite by experts in cetacean systematics using multiple morphological characters. DNA from the identified cetacean tissue samples was extracted and the targeted DNA was sequenced. The researchers then sequenced the DNA of samples from whale products ("unknowns") sold at retail markets in Japan and the Republic of (South) Korea. By comparing the genetic sequences of the unknowns with the known sequences, the researchers could infer the similarity and species identification of the meat in the "whale" products.

Analysis of 655 products revealed meat from baleen whales (eight species or subspecies), sperm whales, pygmy sperm whales, beaked whales (two species), porpoises, killer whales, dolphins (numerous species), and sharks, as well as from domestic sheep and horses (Baker et al., 2000).

Figure 4.5 Several dishes made from different cuts of whale meat.

1. What types of biotechnology techniques were used to investigate products sold as whale meat?

   The biotechnology techniques used are DNA extraction, PCR, and sequencing of samples. These DNA sequences are then aligned and compared to other sequences using bioinformatics procedures.

2. The researchers combined systematics with the use of biotechnology to do their forensic work. Define systematics.

   Systematics is an analytical approach to understanding the diversity and relationships of organisms, both present-day and extinct. It is the study of evolutionary relationships among different groups of organisms based on multiple characteristics, often expressed as phylogenetic trees.

3. Why was it important for a systematist to identify the "known" cetacean species from which DNA was extracted and sequenced?

   By having an expert do the identifications, the database of sequences is more valid. Systematists look at many characters in making an identification, not just a sequence of DNA that may or may not be expressed.

4. Based on your reading in the case, why do you think vendors would substitute horse meat for whale meat in some of the Asian markets?

   Because whale meat is hard to obtain, it is expensive. Vendors can increase profits by substituting cheaper, more readily available meat for the more expensive whale meat.

B. How Is the Analysis of Whale Products Done? This next investigation introduces forensic tools that were used to study whale products, as well as some of the reasoning processes used by systematists to develop hypotheses about relationships.

In our whale meat example, the task of species identification began with isolating DNA from the unknown meat and then looking for a tiny portion of the genomic DNA. A mitochondrial DNA (mtDNA) control region (shaded, Figure 4.6) consisting of only 500 base pairs (bp) was targeted.

Although much of this region is highly conserved (retained with few differences among species), known differences within a hypervariable subsection of the region were used to distinguish among cetacean species.

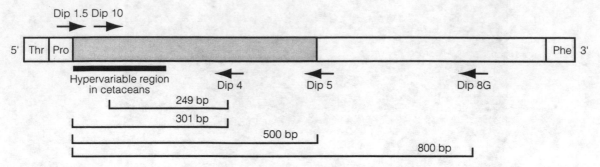

Figure 4.6 A schematic map of the mtDNA control region as well as the binding sites and orientation of the primers used in isolating cetacean DNA. The shaded region represents the portion of the control region covered by most sequences in the reference data sets.

Researchers used PCR to amplify the target mtDNA sequence in the unknown meats. The target mtDNA was then sequenced and aligned with the data set of known cetacean sequences for this segment of DNA. A computer program first compared the target sequence of the sample to known cetacean sequences. Then the program generated a model based on the overall similarities between the target sequence and known cetacean sequences (Figure 4.7).

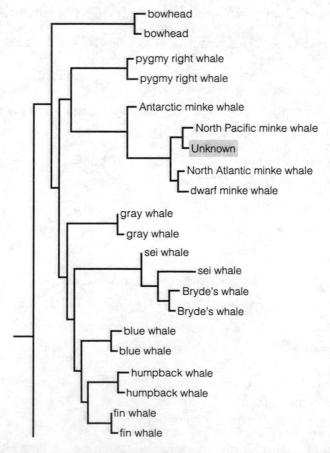

Figure 4.7 Resulting genetic similarity tree showing relative position of unknown samples. Note that the genetic similarity within species is shown by multiple samples in known species, for example, blue whale samples.

1. Which cetacean does the unknown sample most closely match?

   North Pacific minke whale

   The Convention on International Trade in Endangered Species (CITES) works to conserve endangered species by regulating and, where necessary, banning international trade. International trade is banned for those species threatened with extinction. International trade in species that are less endangered or that may become so, is permitted when properly regulated. (Note: The cetacean identified in your answer to question 1 is found in the second group.)

2. Phylogenetic trees are hypotheses that show a pattern of evolutionary relationships, based on analyses of multiple characters, for multiple taxa. A phylogenetic tree implies a chronological sequence of divergence (branching). Explain why Figure 4.7 is not a phylogenetic tree.

   No, it is not a phylogenetic tree. Phylogenetic trees are based on analyses of multiple characteristics for multiple taxa. Figure 4.7 is based on a tiny fragment of DNA found in these taxa. This tree can still be used to infer relationships, but without consideration of relative time.

3. Divergence of cetacean species occurred within the last 50 to 65 million years (O'Leary and Geisler, 1999). Explain the difference between the use of a fragment of hypervariable mitochondrial DNA as a molecular marker and the use of a gene such as the one that encodes for hemoglobin. How might you use each of these to compare DNA sequences between cetaceans and other organisms? (*Hint:* See the information in Chapter 26 on molecular clocks.)

   Fifty to sixty-five million years is a relatively short time in the evolutionary scale. The hypervariable fragment changes relatively frequently and is a good molecular marker for relatively recent events in evolutionary history because the molecule shows changes over a short period of time. In the textbook reading, students will learn that hemoglobin is slow to change (highly conserved), and much is known about its rate of change. This molecular marker is useful as a molecular probe with a regular rate of change (clock) to compare changes in taxa over a longer period of time.

4. An attorney defending a whale meat supplier accused of improperly labeling meat would most likely claim that the inferences drawn from the prosecution's evidence were questionable. Provide a potential argument that specifically describes a weakness in the methodology used to infer species identity of the whale meat in this investigation.

   The whale market researchers used only a tiny fragment of a single piece of mitochondrial DNA. Is this really a defensible way to identify species? They might also call into question the systematics experts who did the on-site identifications. Did they know what they were doing? Could they have made a mistake?

5. How might the prosecuting attorney answer this argument? (*Note:* Defend the methodology that was criticized above.)

   The researchers did use a tiny fragment of DNA; however, to establish the identifications of the reference DNA sequences from known cetacean sources, they used expert systematists who identified the animals based on multiple morphological characters. This lends weight to the validity of the inferences drawn from the genetic similarity tree. The systematists would need to be shown to be of good standing and respected in their field.

C. Going Further: Testing Unknowns with "Witness for the Whales." At the website "Witness for the Whales," users can submit unknown mtDNA sequences to be compared against known cetacean sequences. Genetic similarity analyses can be performed. Results are returned in tree and table format, summarizing the genetic distances between the unknown and reference sequences. (Go to the Case Book website for access to and instructions for "Witness for the Whales.")

Note to instructors: Students may choose to submit one of several unknowns for identification at "Witness for the Whales." You could use this as an opportunity for comparing other morphological characters and create a cladogram to compare with those generated using DNA sequences. (See the Whippo exercise on the Case Book website.)

III. Which Mammals Are Related Most Closely to Whales?

A. The Ungulates. Most scientists agree that whales are members of the ungulates, or hoofed mammals. Some evidence suggests that whales share a common ancestor that gave rise to other living ungulates such as deer, rhinoceroses, horses, camels, pigs, and hippopotamuses. The relationship between whales and other ungulate taxa is still under investigation (O'Leary and Geisler, 1999).

The ungulates are divided into two orders. Horses, zebras, tapirs, and rhinoceroses are odd-toed hoofed mammals, still known as the Perissodactyla. Even-toed ungulates such as deer, sheep, pigs, and cows are known as the Artiodactyla. Until recently, systematists considered Artiodactyla and Cetacea as two distinct mammalian orders. However, several sources of scientific data support the idea that whales are closely related to the members of Artiodactyla. Artiodactyls and cetaceans are now placed in the same order—Cetartiodactyla. The idea of whales sharing an ancestor with these ungulates would seem unlikely if we compared anatomy in living species only.

1. List three characters that you could observe in living whales that white-tailed deer or other even-toed ungulates do not seem to share.

   Students will provide many different answers: limbs designed for swimming, no adult body hair, blubber, fusiform body shape, blowholes, smooth skin, ability to hold breath a long time, some whales are baleen (filter) feeders, not browsers.

2. Molecular data can also be used to examine relationships between organisms, but the inaccessibility of comparative DNA samples for extinct taxa limits the usefulness of these data. Evidence for shared characters between whales and ungulates based on protein or nucleic acid sequences involves sampling of extant taxa only. However, whale skeletal data incorporate extensive paleontological data from fossils as well as data from extant species. Scientists use fossil data to help reconstruct the hypothetical relationships among whales and other even-toed ungulate taxa. This is a valuable source of data, because like many other taxa, most of the even-toed ungulates that have existed are now extinct.

   Name a character you would expect to find in fossils of early whales that would provide evidence that whales share a common ancestor with other even-toed ungulates.

   Features might include the presence of hind limbs with an even number of toes, teeth with an overall similarity to other ungulate dentition, or hooves.

B. Explore Whale Evolution with the Whippo Problem Space. A good place to begin exploring the relationship between whales and other mammals is the Whippo Problem Space at the BEDROCK bioinformatics education site (see the Case Book website for access information). This Whippo site organizes diverse resources including data and tools to support inquiry.

Consider Figure 4.8. Examine the two trees carefully. Each represents different hypotheses about the evolutionary relationships among the whales and various ungulates. Note that although there are differences in branching patterns (tree shape), both trees include the same outgroup.

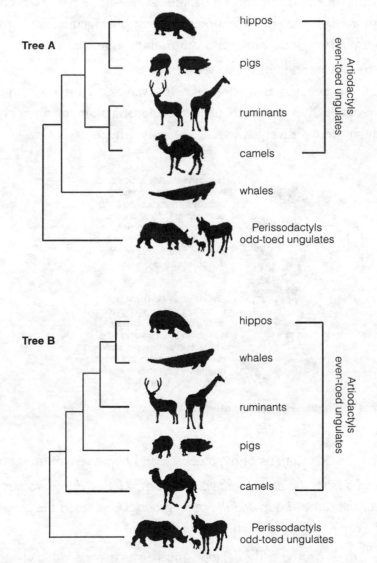

Figure 4.8 Phylogenetic tree representing different hypotheses about the relationships between artiodactyls, the even-toed ungulates. Note the position of whales in each.

1. What is the hypothesized outgroup for both trees?

Perissodactyls, or odd-toed ungulates

2. Which tree shows whales and hippos sharing the closest relationship?

Tree B

3. *Tree thinking* is a term biologists use to describe the process of approaching biological problem solving by considering the role of descent with modification based on phylogenetic evidence. This can result in controversies such as that surrounding the evolution of birds. Did the clade that includes birds diverge from a particular group of dinosaurs? Or did it diverge from a line of reptiles that did not include dinosaurs? These types of questions have fueled much debate and extensive research efforts for decades. Because multiple sources of data exist, both the conclusions reached and the trees drawn by independent researchers may not agree. Not only the selection but also the interpretation of characters can support different phylogenies. Biologists try to resolve these questions by carefully weighing evidence from multiple sources.

Look closely at the tree shape in Figure 4.9. When you investigate the reasonableness of a tree, you should examine all the hypotheses it contains (Donovan and Hornack, 2004). Each branch point in the tree represents a hypothesis about the relationships among members of the ungulates. The order in which groups diverged is also an explicit hypothesis.

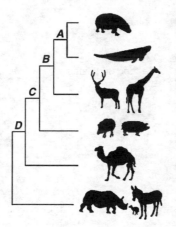

Hypothesis A: Hippos and whales shared a common ancestor more recently with each other than with other ungulates. The two groups have since diverged. Each possesses derived characters not found in the other groups.

Hypothesis B: The group containing deer and giraffes diverged from the group containing hippos and whales. These two groups also shared a common ancestor, but less recently than the one shared by hippos and whales.

Figure 4.9 Hypotheses in tree B (Figure 4.8) represented by the letters A, B, C, and D.

After you have reviewed the descriptions of hypothesis A and hypothesis B, describe hypothesis D.

Camels as a group diverged from the group containing hippos, whales, deer, giraffes, pigs, and tapirs. The common ancestor of the camel group and the other group is older than the common ancestors at A, B, or C; therefore, the camels diverged from the others earlier.

4. What does hypothesis D tell us about the relationship between perissodactyls and artiodactyls?

The ancestor to camels and the other artiodactyls diverged relatively early from the perissodactyls.

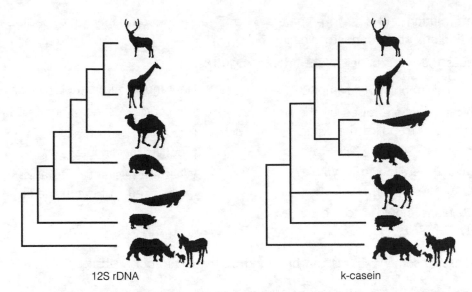

Figure 4.10 Different phylogenetic trees based on select genetic sequences for different molecules. (*Note:* You can read more about tree interpretation on the Whippo site.)

5. Which of the trees based on molecular sequence data shown in Figure 4.10 supports hypothesis A in tree B? Explain.

   The k-casein tree shows the common ancestor for whales and hippos to be more recent than ancestors they share with other ungulates. The 12S rDNA tree does not support hypothesis A. Although whales and hippos share a common ancestor, other ungulates (deer, giraffes, and camels) also share this ancestor.

6. Does either tree in Figure 4.10 support hypothesis B in tree B? Explain.

   The k-casein tree does support hypothesis B because the deer and giraffes share a common ancestor with hippos and whales less recently than the one shared by hippos and whales. The 12S rDNA tree does not support the hypothesis.

7. Do you think molecular sequence data are helpful characters to use to infer phylogenetic relationships? What concerns might you have if a tree were based on a single molecule?

   Molecular sequence data are helpful, but these data should be considered carefully. Molecules change over time at different rates. Some are quite highly conserved. Certainly any tree based on a single character is incomplete, and it is better to include an array of characters. Molecular data from extinct forms are not available except in special instances of preservation.

Additional Investigation

IV. Position Paper on Whaling

Explore the management of whaling in the modern world. Explain the role of biotechnology and systematics in increasing the global potential for biologically sustainable management of whale populations. Introduce two or more historical, cultural, economic, political, or ethical issues that should be addressed by policies governing whaling practices. Include reliable resources of data on whale population biology.

Reason from information and data to prepare a 3- to 5-page position paper that specifically addresses your findings about modern whaling policy.

Examples of issues that your paper might address include:

- How are whale populations sampled?
- What ethical issues are raised by the use of biotechnology to police the whale market?
- Should anyone be allowed to whale? Why or why not?
- Which cetaceans should or could be harvested?

- How much might they be harvested?
- Are cetacean sanctuaries feasible?
- Is the U.S. ban on all marine mammal products reasonable?
- What are relevant cultural issues that might need to be considered?

Resources and links to some websites can be found on the Case Book website.

(*Note:* Your instructor may assign this as a class debate.)

Note to instructors: There are several ways to use this investigation. You could have students work independently. You could also have a group of students research separate components and then combine their information in a single paper or presentation. For very large classes you might use this as a class discussion to assess your students' grasp of the impact of biotechnology and systematics in the modern world. Consider this activity as a class debate.

V. Open-Ended Investigations

A. Four new species of additional Dendrogrammaceae have been discovered. How might this change your phylogram? Evolution can include both acquisition and loss of traits, so more than one cladogram may be possible without further information.

B. Consider using Biology Workbench (http://workbench.sdsc.edu) to explore the relationships between cetaceans and taxa other than artiodactyle using genes from the same mitrochondrial control region.

References

Baker, C. S., G. M. Lento, F. Cipriano, and S. R. Palumbi. 2000. Predicted decline of protected whales based on molecular genetic monitoring of Japanese and Korean markets. *Proceedings of the Royal Society of London B* 267 (1449): 1191–1199, 2000.

Baker, C. S., M. L. Dalebout, G. M. Lento, and N. Funahashi. 2002. Gray whale products sold in commercial markets along the Pacific Coast of Japan. *Marine Mammal Science* 18:295–300, 2002.

Donovan, S., and D. Hornack. 2004. Losing the forest for the trees: Learning to compare trees and assess support for phylogenetic hypotheses. Poster. NABT National Conference, 2004.

O'Leary, M. A., and G. H. Geisler. 1999. The position of Cetacea within Mammalia: Phylogenetic analysis of morphological data from extinct and extant taxa. *Systematic Biology* 48(3): 455–490, 1999.

Ross, H. A., G. M. Lento, M. L. Dalebout, M. Goode, G. Ewing, P. McLaren, A. G. Rodrigo, S. Lavery, and C. S. Baker. 2003. DNA surveillance: Web-based molecular identification of whales, dolphins and porpoises. *Journal of Heredity* 94:111–114, 2003.

Wagner, W. H., Jr. 2001. Dendrogrammaceae. In E. D. Stanley, "Visual Data Sets," *BioQUEST Library VI*. San Diego: Academic Press, 2001.

Witness for the Whales. Online at http://www.cebl.auckland.ac.nz:9000/page/whales/title (accessed October 10, 2007).

Chapter 5:

Unveiling the Carboniferous

INSTRUCTOR'S GUIDE

As with all the cases in this book, please read the preface if you have not already done so. In the preface you will find suggestions for using Investigative Case–Based Learning (ICBL) in different instructional situations such as starting a new lecture topic, assessing what students already know, setting a context for lab activities, and so on. The preface also describes ways to use cases in a variety of classroom settings and suggests multiple ways to assess learning with cases.

Unveiling the Carboniferous accompanies Unit Five: The Evolutionary History of Biological Diversity in Campbell and Reece's *Biology*, 8th edition. The case, in which a company develops a mural exhibit depicting the Carboniferous, emphasizes material covered in Chapter 25, Chapter 26, and Chapters 29–34 (plants, fungi, and animals). There are three strands in the case:

- The Carboniferous period
- Major biological events of the Carboniferous
- Terrestrial adaptations in animals and changes in plant communities

Students should complete the Case Analysis immediately following the reading of the case. We strongly suggest that students work in groups to complete the Case Analysis. Actively listening to and challenging the ideas of others can help learners become aware of their own misconceptions, yet also value their own and others' prior knowledge.

Seven investigations accompany *Unveiling the Carboniferous*. Four are "core" investigations relating directly to the facts of the case, two are additional investigations that use Web-based resources or extend the case to other applications, and one is an open-ended investigation in which students explore a different post-Cambrian period. Table IG5.1 describes what students will gain from each investigation.

Table IG5.1 Unveiling the Carboniferous Case Overview.

Investigation	Learning Goals	Inquiry Skills Used
Core Investigations		
I. Critical Reading	Students use the chapters in Unit Five as their primary resource as they develop an overview of the organisms of the Carboniferous.	• identifying key information • applying generalized information to a specific problem • gathering material from different locations in the text to answer questions critical to the case
II. The Carboniferous Globe	Using maps of landforms of ancient Earth, students determine global climatic conditions during the Carboniferous, further developing their understanding of this period.	• combining information from other disciplines (geoscience, meteorology) to develop a global understanding of this period
III. Adaptations in the Carboniferous	Students address two major adaptations: the amniotic egg and insect wings. They research images and describe the significance of the adaptations.	• identifying information • synthesizing facts from disparate sources • making inferences about significance
IV. Coal Connections	Students learn how coal balls form and how data from coal balls can be used to explain when the coal was formed.	• evaluating how the data may be valuable for this project • using knowledge of paleobotany to infer ages of coal balls
Additional Investigations		
V. Calculating Scale Bars and Magnifications	Students practice calculating scale values and magnification from images of fossils. Scale will affect their choices of organisms to illustrate in the mural.	• measuring • applying mathematics to biological images and objects • calculating size and magnification
VI. Educational Resources to Accompany the Mural	The mural project is to be a community and educational resource. Students develop a Web page, a visitors' brochure, or a classroom activity.	• making complicated science accessible to nonscientists (a key skill for biologists)
VII. Open-Ended Investigations	Students use a wide variety of resources to plan a brochure, mural, image, or time line for a different period.	• identifying and locating appropriate information • transforming these data into a different format

Table IG5.2 contains several resources related to *Biology*, 8th edition, that will help your students further their understanding of this case. Note that chapter readings and activities are listed in order of importance.

Table IG5.2 Campbell-Related Resources.

Resource	Chapter/Activity	Topics Covered/Activity Title
Critical Reading from *Biology*, 8th edition	Chapter 25: The History of Life on Earth	Table 25.1: The Geologic Record; the fossil record (Concept 25.3); continental drift (Concept 25.4)
	Chapter 29: Plant Diversity I: How Plants Colonized Land	Figure 29.5: Derived traits of land plants (Concept 29.1); bryophytes (Concept 29.2); origins and traits of vascular plants; classification of seedless vascular plants; Figure 29.16: drawing of Carboniferous forest (Concept 29.3)
	Chapter 30: Plant Diversity II: The Evolution of Seed Plants	Evolutionary advantage of seeds (Concept 30.1); gymnosperms (Concept 30.2)
Related Readings	Chapter 31: Fungi	First evidence of mycorrhizae (Concept 31.3)
	Chapter 32: An Introduction to Animal Diversity	History of animals (Concept 32.2)
	Chapter 33: Invertebrates	Students will find many answers to Table 5.1 in this chapter.
	Chapter 34: Vertebrates	Students will find many answers to Table 5.1 in this chapter. Also important: tetrapods (Concept 34.5); amniotes (Concept 34.6)
Campbell website/ CD-ROM	Chapter 25 **Activity**	The History of Life
	Chapter 29 **Activity**	Terrestrial Adaptations of Plants
	Chapter 30 **Activity**	Pine Life Cycle

Case Narrative

Students were asked to underline terms or phrases in the introductory narrative that they think are important to understanding the case. Suggested terms and phrases that students might have chosen are in bold type.

Memorandum

To: Miles Harrington, BioConsulting Associates

Re: Carboniferous Mural

Date: November 19, 2008

Enclosed are comments on the **mural design** for the new science building at Colter College. The stated goals of the mural project are to: (1) situate well in the local community, (2) relate to the donor's connection to the **coal industry,** and (3) serve as a **resource for teaching** science.

The **Carboniferous period** is an appropriate choice for the mural, as there is a strong scientific connection to the region's history of **coal mining** and the donor's interests. However, your drawings of a **swampy forest** of the Carboniferous fall short. A similar conception of the Carboniferous is found in many museums, but it **fails to emphasize several significant events** of the period. Further, it **gives the impression of a single climate—tropical—when in fact there were major glaciations with corresponding drops in sea level and increases in arid zones. Fossils of the period** provide evidence of **adaptive radiation of previously established terrestrial organisms** such as **seed plants, tetrapods, and insects.**

The **climatic changes** in the Carboniferous were a significant **factor in the evolution of plant communities,** which changed in composition during wet and dry periods. During the periods of ice age, the vast **swamps diminished as drier upland habitats became available.** Instead of tree-size lycophytes—a common feature of tropical swamps—**conifers and seed ferns were dominant species forming the upland forest.** Throughout the period, a wide **variety of structural adaptations resulted in taller plants.**

Although **internal fertilization** was well established previously, the **first amniotes** were tetrapods that produced **shelled eggs during the Carboniferous.** This enabled reproduction as well as embryonic development away from water for both **synapsids** (reptilelike ancestors to modern mammals) and **reptiles.** Another major development during the early Carboniferous was **flight in insects.** A tremendous **radiation of flying insects** is seen in the fossil record by the end of the Carboniferous.

While the Carboniferous was a time during which **terrestrial habitats were well exploited** by an increasing variety of life forms, keep in mind that **many of the early adaptations for living on land,** such as the insect exoskeleton, tetrapod body shape, and plant vascular tissue, **arose during earlier geologic periods.**

We think that Wall Works, Inc., has a real opportunity to create a mural that richly illuminates the Carboniferous in a way that can serve the regional and educational communities. Let us know if we can be of further assistance.

"Well, this certainly changes things," Dericia thought as she prepared the agenda for the next design meeting. "Maybe we should consider **multiple panels** and involve the biology department from Colter College." She anticipated lively discussion at the next meeting.

Suggested Answers for Case Analysis

1. **Recognize potential issues and major topics in the case.** What is this case about? Underline terms or phrases that seem to be important to understanding this case. Then list **3 or 4** biology-related topics or issues in the case.

   Biology-related topics or issues: the timing and conditions of the Carboniferous, further adaptations for survival on land, biological events of the Carboniferous, teaching with murals.

2. **What specific questions do you have about these topics?** By yourself, or better yet, in a group, make a list of what you already know about this case in the "What Do I Know?" column. List questions you would like to learn more about in the "What Do I Need to Know?" column.

   There are many possible answers, depending on the experience of your students. Some likely responses follow.

What Do I Know?	What Do I Need to Know?
• *Coal is from the Carboniferous. (Note: This is not strictly correct because coal was formed in other periods as well, but students are likely to state this.)*	• *How long ago was the Carboniferous?*
• *There were amphibians, treelike plants, and insects.*	• *What organisms lived during the Carboniferous?*
• *Fossils exist from that time.*	• *What was the world like then?*
• *Organisms lived on land.*	• *Were there dinosaurs?*
• *Earth was hot and swampy. (Note: While this is a misconception when considering the entire globe, it is a likely student response.)*	• *How are fossils formed?*
	• *What are the problems of living on land?*
	• *How do you design a mural?*
• *The continents were in different places than they are now.*	• *What evidence supports the mural?*
• *The fossil record is spotty and incomplete.*	

3. Put a check mark by **1–3** questions or issues from the "What Do I Need to Know?" list that you think are most important to explore.

   You should expect a range of responses. Most students will use the contextual clues of being in a biology class and beginning the diversity of life unit to identify questions about fossils and adaptations.

4. **What kinds of references or resources would help you answer or explore these questions?** Identify two different resources and explain what information each resource is likely to give that will help you answer the question(s). Choose specific resources.

   Accept any reasonable resource (e.g., text, other book, Internet sites, maps, data tables, and so on) that could be related to this case. The answer "the Web" is too vague. Students should explain the type of site they are looking for or search terms they might use.

Suggested Answers for Core Investigations

I. Critical Reading

You will need to use information from several chapters in Unit Five, as well as the geologic record table in Chapter 25 (Table 25.1), to answer the following questions. You may also want to refer to some of the Web links provided for this unit on the Case Book website.

The biology department decided to have students work on the mural project. The students began by familiarizing themselves with the organisms likely to have lived during the Carboniferous. From looking at images such at Figure 29.16 and reading the caption, the students knew that some insects, as well as lycophytes, horsetails, and tree ferns, were present. Examine Table 25.1 to answer the following questions. You may need to use the index to find information on specific organisms within other chapters of the unit.

1. How long ago was the Carboniferous?

   359–299 million years ago

2. List five other terrestrial organisms (not listed elsewhere in this case) that likely lived during the Carboniferous. Include organisms from at least three kingdoms. You may use common names.

   Note: This question is to encourage students to look at many chapters in Unit Five, and to allow students to realize that many organisms not seen in Figure 29.16 proliferated during this time period. We want them to identify groups not commonly seen in images of the Carboniferous. Many correct answers exist. Just look for obvious errors, for example, dinosaurs, humans, other mammals, birds, and flowering plants. Examples of correct answers include: algae, protists, archaea, fungi (including mycorrhizae), lichens, bacteria, reptiles, conifers, bryophytes (mosses, liverworts), amphibians, and many invertebrates.

3. List four animal phyla that you would expect to find living in the aquatic environments of the Carboniferous including swamps and oceans.

   Examples include chordates (any subgroup such as sharks, lancelets, and fish), molluscs, echinoderms, platyhelminthes, nematodes, annelids, porifera, cnidarians, arthropods.

4. At the first meeting, the artists from Wall Works gave the biology students a list of organisms from their image files. Please evaluate whether or not the organisms listed in Table 5.1 would be appropriate for the mural of the Carboniferous.

Table IG5.3 Answers to Student Table 5.1.

Type of Organism	Era and Period in Which Organism Is Thought to Have Originated	Present in the Carboniferous? (Yes or No)
Amphibian	Paleozoic, Devonian	Yes
Bird	Mesozoic, Late Jurassic	No
Conifer	Paleozoic, Carboniferous	Yes
Dinosaur	Mesozoic, Triassic	No
Grass	Mesozoic, Cretaceous	No
Horsetail	Paleozoic, Ordovician	Yes

Human	Cenozoic, Neogene	No
Insect	Paleozoic, Ordovician	Yes
Jawed fish	Paleozoic, Ordovician	Yes
Lycophyte	Paleozoic, Ordovician	Yes
Moss	Paleozoic, Ordovician	Yes
Mycorrhizae	Paleozoic, Silurian	Yes
Saber-tooth cat	Cenozoic, Paleogene	No
Spider	Paleozoic, Ordovician	Yes
Sponge	Proterozoic	Yes
Trilobite	Paleozoic, Cambrian	Yes

5. Suggest some reasons for the absence today of dog-size amphibians, tree-size club mosses, and giant dragonflies.

Expect a wide range of answers. Most students will probably mention climatic changes. As a result of changes in climate, the swamps dried up and temperatures became cooler. The concentration of oxygen in the atmosphere was higher in the Carboniferous than it is today, which enabled insects to grow large. In addition, the radiation of predators impacted these species.

II. The Carboniferous Globe

The Carboniferous, originally named for the rich deposits of coal found in strata of that period in England, is divided into the Lower Carboniferous (or early, often called the Mississippian by researchers in North America) and the Upper Carboniferous (or late, often called the Pennsylvanian by researchers in North America). Limestone deposits laid down on the floors of shallow seas characterize the Lower Carboniferous, whereas coal deposits formed from organisms in swampy forests characterize the Upper Carboniferous. Ongoing glaciation events changed the sea levels during the Carboniferous; therefore, it is not unusual to find some limestone layers interspersed with the coal in Upper Carboniferous deposits.

To get a better idea of what the globe looked like during the Carboniferous, consider Figure 25.13 in the text on the history of continental drift. You could also refer to the Paleomap Project website in the Case Book portion of the Campbell website.

1. Which of the four global landmasses shown in Figure 25.13 corresponds to the Carboniferous?

Pangaea, the landmass present during the late Paleozoic

Additional information is provided by Figure 5.1, which is an evidence-based map of the landmasses during the Upper Carboniferous, with overlay outlines of climate. Several kinds of geologic formations are shown. The small gray circles represent Upper Carboniferous coal beds. The locations of Colter College and its sister college in present-day Scotland are shown.

During the late Paleozoic, the supercontinent Pangaea formed. Not only the position but also the climate of present-day continents were quite different at that time. Not every region had conditions that led to the formation of coal. Use Figure 5.1 to answer the following questions.

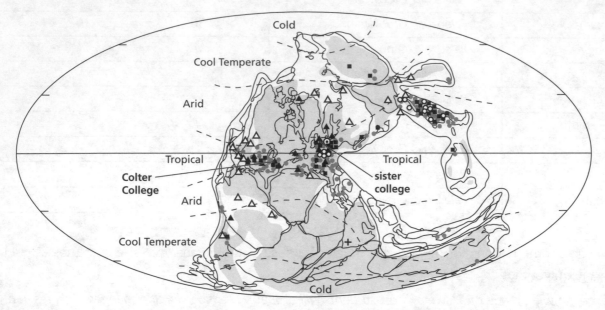

Figure 5.1 The globe during the Upper Carboniferous, showing location of landmasses and climatic conditions.

2. Consider the map in Figure 5.1 carefully. Are there geographic and/or climatic similarities between Colter College and its sister college in Scotland? Explain.

   Both were tropical and likely shared similar coal forests. Many coal deposits are shown near each.

3. Why don't we find Upper Carboniferous coal deposits in present-day South America, India, Australia, Africa, and Antarctica? What was the climate like in these areas during the Upper Carboniferous?

   It was very cold or very dry in what would become southern Africa, South America, India, Australia, and Antarctica. Conditions did not support the formation of swamp forests; therefore, no coal was formed.

4. The first recorded use of coal occurred about 3,000 years ago at the Fushun mine in northeastern China. At that time, the people thought of coal as just a remarkable stone that could burn. Based on Figure 5.1, where do you think the land that is now China was located during the Carboniferous? Explain your reasoning.

   The landmass that is now China was most likely located at the farthest right landmass on the map, above the equator, where many coal deposits are shown.

III. Adaptations in the Carboniferous

Many adaptations contributed to the success of life on land. In the case, Miles Harrington mentioned some important adaptations of amniotic eggs and insect wings seen for the first time during the Carboniferous.

1. For the two adaptations listed, attach an image of an organism with this feature that is thought to have existed during the Carboniferous. Write what type of organism it is and explain why the adaptation was significant to the success of the organism.

Adaptation: Amniotic eggs

Image Source: *Many possible answers. Some of the Web links in the Case Book website will have images.*

Type: *Students may have chosen a reptile or a basal synapsid, both amniotes.*

Significance: *The amniotic egg can be laid on dry ground. The egg retains moisture for the embryo and allows the embryo to develop in the absence of water. Amniotic eggs are oxygen-permeable, allowing for the high metabolic activity needed for development. The internal membranes assist in storage of nitrogenous wastes, which are converted to uric acid. Internal fertilization is found in amniotes (and some other organisms). Internal fertilization prevents gametes from drying out and permits reproductive use of terrestrial habitats far from water.*

Adaptation: Insect wings

Image Source: *Figure 29.16 has a dragonfly, as well as other winged insects. Many appropriate images may be found on the Internet.*

Type: *Many insect orders including beetles, dragonflies, others*

Significance: *Flying insects have a mechanism to escape some predators and access food sources available on taller plants.*

2. During the Carboniferous, forests grew to unprecedented heights. Describe one adaptation in plants that would account for this dramatic change.

Most students will answer "vascular tissue." They might also mention that vascular tissues conduct both water and nutrients to all parts of the plant and provide support. Plants with more extensive root, stem, and leaf systems increased by the end of the Carboniferous.

IV. Coal Connections

1. Why do we refer to coal as a "fossil fuel"?

Coal is the product of organic debris that accumulated in vast swamps of the past, forming layers of peat. Eventually, over millions of years, these deposits turned into coal. Most coal deposits were formed in the Carboniferous period.

In the case, the coal deposits mined near Colter College are from the Upper Carboniferous period, more than 299 million years ago. In highly compressed coal (high-grade coal), the original plant materials and traces of fossils have been obscured. In contrast, coal balls, which are formed when soluble mineral compounds such as silicates and carbonates infiltrate plant tissues, contain fossils with much detail, including microscopic structures (see Figure 5.2).

Analysis of coal ball fossils found in the Colter College area may be helpful because both plant and, occasionally, invertebrate animal fossils may be included. Plant fossils from many Carboniferous coal ball deposits retain permineralized microstructure at the cellular and subcellular levels. Note that it is a matter of chance as to which organisms are fossilized in coal balls. Although it is very difficult to accurately infer population sizes from coal ball analysis, the variety of plant materials seen in a coal ball may provide information about when the coal was formed. For example, if you were to compare coal ball material with modern peat samples you should expect to see significant differences in the plant groups.

Figure 5.2 Fossilized plant materials can be observed in remarkably fine detail using an acetate peel of a coal ball. In this image you can see the cross section of a stem.

2. You observe samples from two coal balls collected in different places. Sample 1 contains roots and stems of tree-size lycophytes and horsetails. Sample 2 contains evidence of sphagnum moss "leaves," yellow cedar needles, and alder pollen. From what time period do you think each sample originated? Explain your answer.

    Sample 1 is consistent with Carboniferous coal balls. Tree-size lycophytes and horsetails no longer exist. Sample 2 is consistent with a much later time period, including the present. Although Sphagnum (peat moss) is a bryophyte and yellow cedar is a gymnosperm, alder is an angiosperm. Angiosperms did not evolve until after the Carboniferous.

Suggested Answers for Additional Investigations

V. Calculating Scale Bars and Magnifications

To increase the scientific accuracy and to allow comparisons of the relative sizes of the organisms featured in the mural, you are asked to provide a scale bar or magnification for each of the fossils the artists will be using.

If you work with an image that is its actual size (magnification = 1), drawing a scale bar is fairly straightforward. You would draw a 1-inch line as the scale bar and label the scale value as 1 inch, indicating that an inch on the image equals 1 inch of the actual fossil. However, most images are not shown at their actual size because the subject is either too small or too large for the medium. Scale bars, magnification values, and objects of known size allow the viewer to consider the actual size of the subject.

Figure 5.3 Leaf fossil with penny to show scale.

1. You can determine both the image magnification and the size of a fossil specimen if an object of known size is included in the image. In Figure 5.3, the penny has a known diameter of 0.75 in. However, in this image the penny measures only 0.5 inch across. Now you know that the image is smaller than its actual size. In fact, the magnification is 0.67 times its actual size. (See calculations below.)

   Magnification = diameter of the penny in the image/actual diameter of a penny

   Magnification = 0.50 inch/0.75 inch

   Magnification = 0.67×

   Now estimate the actual length of the leaf fossil using the penny for scale. Use the following calculation.

   Actual leaf fossil length = image length/image magnification

   The leaf is approximately 2.75 inches long. The diameter of the penny fits about 5.5 times across the leaf. Actual fossil length = 2.75 inches/0.67×

   = 4.10 inches

2. Figure 5.4 shows a fossil of footprints made by an anthracosaur, an amphibian from the Upper Carboniferous. We can calculate the magnification of this image because we know that the scale bar (black and white strip) measures 1 inch long with a value of 10.5 cm (each stripe on the bar is 5 mm wide). By doing the calculations below, we can conclude that this image is about one-fourth its actual size.

   Magnification = scale bar length/scale value

   Magnification = 1 inch/10.5 cm

   (*Note:* Convert to same units.)

   Magnification = 2.54 cm/10.5 cm

   Magnification = 0.24×

Figure 5.4 Fossilized anthracosaur footprints.

Students examine a problem that is already completed for them. No answer required.

3. While searching for images, you find a drawing of an early swamp with a dragonfly. The caption says the dragonfly has a wingspan of 2 feet. Use 2 feet as the scale value. The size of the dragonfly wingspan measured from this image is 0.5 inch. Use this value for the length of the scale bar. What is the total magnification of this image?

Magnification = scale bar length/scale value

Magnification = 0.5 inch/2 feet

Magnification = 0.5 inch/24 inches

Magnification = 0.021 times the actual size

4. a. Figure 5.5 is an image of a fossilized echinoderm. Estimate the actual diameter of the fossil. (*Note:* Measure from left arm to right arm.)

   Using the scale bar, the diameter is approximately 15 mm or 1.5 cm.

   b. If a penny has an actual diameter of 0.75 inch, how many times would this fossil fit across the diameter of a penny?

   A little more than one time. The penny has a diameter of 19 mm.

Figure 5.5 Fossilized invertebrate.

5. The wall space for the mural measures 10 feet high by 20 feet wide. You wish to include a 40-m-tall lycophyte and a "giant horsetail" at 15 meters tall. To determine which of the magnifications would allow you to fit these organisms in the mural, use the height of the wall as the scale bar length and the height of the tallest organism as your scale value. Which of the following magnifications would allow you to include these organisms?

(a) 3×   (b) 0.5×   (c) 0.1×   (d) 0.075×

The answer is (d). Magnification = scale bar length/scale value = 10 feet/40 meters

Magnification = 3 meters/40 meters = 0.075×

6. You suggest a scale bar that is 1 foot long for the final mural. What is the approximate value of this scale bar in meters?

(a) 0.4 m   (b) 1 m   (c) 4 m   (d) 10 m

The answer is (c). Scale value = 1 foot/0.0753

Scale value = 13.333 feet = 4.06 m

7. Now that you know the dimensions of the mural and the magnification that accommodates the largest trees, what size would a 1-foot-long reptile be in the mural?

An organism 1 foot long in life would be 0.9 inch long in the mural. This is very small and may not be clearly visible from 4 feet away.

8. Artists often use insets (small internal drawings) to change the magnification of a portion of a larger drawing. If you wish to show this reptile and its 1-inch-long egg, what magnification might you choose for an inset? Explain.

Probably nothing smaller than 13, and students should consider larger magnifications.

VI. Educational Resources to Accompany the Mural

One of the goals of the mural project is to be a resource for science education. After meeting with the artists, the biology students accepted the challenge to develop some resources for explaining the mural to visitors, such as local schoolchildren.

The students proposed a mural-related website and some classroom resources. In addition, they saw the need for an interpretive brochure to be used by visitors of the mural itself. These are good ideas, but they need to be researched, designed, and developed. Develop one of the following resources and submit your project as a paper, poster, or slideshow or in another format your instructor suggests.

A. a visitors' brochure (finished product is 2 sides of a standard sheet of paper);

B. a home page for the website, showing the main categories of links, with one example for each; or

C. a classroom activity, not computer-based, indicating grade level, subject matter, materials needed, procedure, and samples of handouts.

1. For the resource you selected, answer the following questions:
   - Who is your audience?
   - How do you expect people will use this resource?
   - What are their likely questions?
   - What information can the resource provide to make the mural a richer experience?
   - What are the strengths and weaknesses of this kind of resource?

2. Explain your rationale for the design of the resource. Justify the content decisions as well as the layout decisions. For example, you might argue that it is important to develop a social perspective. This might justify links to a local coal miners' museum included on the website, even though this is not biological information.

Note: Students could present their products and their background rationales as posters instead of traditional papers. They should have a usable product (website plan, brochure, or lesson plan). They could develop these projects in groups or individually. You might collaborate with an English or art class to have the presentations juried by peers.

VII. Open-Ended Investigations

Use at least three resources to investigate a different post-Cambrian period in order to plan a brochure, mural, time line, or image.

Chapter 6:

Corn Under Construction

INSTRUCTOR'S GUIDE

As with all the cases in this book, please read the preface if you have not already done so. In the preface you will find suggestions for using Investigative Case–Based Learning (ICBL) in different instructional situations such as starting a new lecture topic, assessing what students already know, setting a context for lab activities, and so on. The preface also describes ways to use cases in a variety of classroom settings and suggests multiple ways to assess learning with cases.

Corn Under Construction accompanies Unit Six: Plant Form and Function in Campbell and Reece's *Biology,* 8th edition. The case, which is about *Bt* corn, emphasizes material in Chapter 38: Angiosperm Reproduction and Biotechnology, and provides cues to students to read selected sections from other chapters in Unit Six and sections of Unit Three on genetic engineering. Students begin the investigative case by reading a narrative about growers at a meeting who are discussing the use of genetically modified (GM) seeds. There are five strands in the case:

- Corn growth and reproduction

- Engineering *Bt* corn

- Making a physical model of corn growth

- Planning refuges

- Consideration of the role of biotechnology in agriculture

Students should complete the Case Analysis immediately following the reading of the case. We strongly suggest that students work in groups to complete the Case Analysis. Actively listening to and challenging the ideas of others can help learners become aware of their own misconceptions, yet also value their own and others' prior knowledge.

Six investigations accompany *Corn Under Construction.* Four are "core" activities relating directly to the facts of the case, one is an additional activity that extends the case to another area of biotechnology, and one open-ended investigation provides opportunities for students to identify a potentially beneficial gene that could be bioengineered into a crop plant. Table IG6.1 describes what students will gain from each investigation.

Table IG6.1 Corn Under Construction Case Overview.

Investigation	Learning Goals	Inquiry Skills Used
Core Investigations		
I. Critical Reading	Students apply information from Chapter 38: Angiosperm Reproduction and Biotechnology to explore issues relating to flowers, pollination, and fruit production in angiosperms.	• mathematical applications to calculate pollen production • interpreting images • applying concepts to new examples • generating alternative explanations
II. Considering *Bt* Corn	The origin of the mystery *Bt* corn in Macon county is explored. Students examine plausibility of several possible explanations for the occurrence. Genetic engineering and plant breeding simulations allow students to compare the two approaches to genetic manipulation of plants. Students also explore the problems of controlling ECB.	• using knowledge to reason about likely explanations for the misplaced *Bt* corn • using free simulations to breed a better ear of corn, or to produce a transgenic plant • interpreting visual data as evidence • developing hypotheses • testing hypotheses • critiquing models
III. Investigating Corn Morphology and Growth with a Model of Insect Damage	Students model corn growth and ECB damage.	• building, using, and critiquing a physical model
IV. Refuges for Resistance Management	Several alternatives for refuge design are provided for students to consider.	• applying concepts to a situation presented in diagrammatic form
Additional Investigation		
V. Making Decisions About DNA Technology: Golden Rice	Students argue for and against the use of transgenic crops in regard to global agriculture.	• critical thinking • constructing logical arguments • considering global issues
VI. Open-Ended Investigations: New genes for crop improvement	Students identify potential genes and their sources that benefit target crop plants	• considering potential improvements in crop plants • using existing gene data and literature to identify potential genes

Table IG6.2 contains several resources related to *Biology*, 8th edition, that will help your students further their understanding of the case. Note that chapter readings and activities are listed in order of importance in regard to the case.

Table IG6.2 Campbell-Related Resources.

Resource	Chapter/Activity	Topics Covered/Activity Titles
Critical Reading from *Biology,* 8th edition	Chapter 38: Angiosperm Reproduction and Biotechnology	Concepts 38.1, 38.3, 38.4 Figures 38.2, 38.8, 38.16
	Chapter 35: Plant Structure, Growth, and Development	Concepts 35.2, 35.3
	Chapter 20: Biotechnology	Genetic Engineering in Plants; Figure 20.25 (Concept 20.4)
Campbell website/ CD-ROM	Chapter 38 **Activities**	Angiosperm Life Cycle Making Decisions About DNA Technology: Golden Rice
	Chapter 23 **Investigation**	How Can Frequency of Alleles Be Calculated?

Case Narrative

Students were asked to underline terms or phrases in the introductory narrative that they think are important to understanding the case. Suggested terms and phrases that students might have chosen are in bold type.

As the local farmers waited for the DeWitt County **Extension** monthly meeting to begin, they began discussing the surprising news that corn containing a **new Bt gene not approved for human consumption** had been found in a **grain elevator** in neighboring Macon County.

"I just don't understand it," Emmet said. "Now those growers **have to sell all the corn in that elevator as animal feed.** How did this happen if **no one in that county planted the new Bt seed?**"

"Well, **they may not plant it in Macon County, but we certainly grow all types of Bt corn here,**" John replied.

"I always get some **volunteer corn** from the year before," Sam offered. "Do you think someone planted new acreage and didn't check for volunteers from the prior owner's crop?"

"I'm pretty sure the **new Bt seed only became available this year,**" Emmet responded. "Do you think the **seed company might have packaged some of the new Bt seed** with the wrong label?"

"I know that **new Bt corn hybrid was planted in at least two fields just north and west of the Macon County border,**" John declared. "So, what about **pollen drift**? Remember how **windy** it was this summer? Why, some of my late-planting corn **seedlings** in the flood plain were knocked down just about the same time the higher-ground corn was **tasseling.**"

The conversation was interrupted as Roger, the county extension agent, signaled for the meeting to start. "Let's get down to today's business—new **alternatives for planting European corn borer refuges**—always a popular topic," he announced with a tentative smile.

Note to instructors: Students will apply concepts they studied in the angiosperm chapter to surmise that pollen drift is the most defensible hypothesis for the problem of the spread of new *Bt* genes.

European corn borers (ECB), which cause many kinds of damage in corn, are mentioned in the case. The problem of ECB damage allows a meaningful introduction of plant growth and morphology covered in this unit. The creation of transgenic crops is also covered in this unit. The information about refuges is an opportunity to study genetic change. While not included in the unit, the problem of the spread of resistance genes in ECB populations lends itself to analysis using the Hardy-Weinberg equation (see Chapter 23 in the text and the Investigation in Chapter 23 of the Campbell website).

European corn borers were introduced accidentally in the United States in 1909. Early control methods centered on burning infected fields and quarantining crops. The discovery that strains of *Bacillus thuringiensis* (*Bt*) produce a toxin effective against the European corn borer (and other lepidopterans) was made in the 1920s. Sprays of whole, dried cultures of *B. thuringiensis* have been used widely to control ECB since the 1930s in conventionally and organically grown corn. Because *Bt* sprays are effective only for a matter of days, use of sprays necessitates repeated scouting in the fields to detect ECB larvae. Most areas of the United States average two to five generations of ECB in a given field each year. Chemical pesticides are less effective than *Bt* spray and are costly and hazardous.

The mid-1990s saw the production of the first transgenic *Bt* corn hybrids. As of 2004, approximately 25% of U.S.-grown corn was *Bt* hybrid corn. A hybrid not approved for human consumption (with a toxin named Cry9C) was grown for feed. Some of this corn was discovered in taco shells and several other corn products. That hybrid has been taken off the market.

Because the continuous expression of the *Bt* gene in corn puts strong selection pressure on the ECB, mutations for resistance are likely to be selected for. The Environmental Protection Agency requires that a refuge of non-*Bt* corn be planted in each field. By maintaining a population of nonresistant ECB in the refuge, the spread of resistance genes is slowed. Some seed companies have suggested that a particular *Bt* hybrid will remain effective for about 3 times as long in fields where growers use refuges. Refuges are required for most transgenic crops and range from 20% to 50% of planted acreage for that crop.

The corn grown in the refuge will mature normally. It will likely be damaged by ECB because the grower is not permitted to spray it with *Bt* spray or use chemical pesticides that could kill ECB. However, the corn is harvested and sold mixed in with the grain produced by the *Bt* hybrids. In fact, due to pollen drift, many of the kernels on the non-*Bt* ears will be *Bt* seeds.

The seed companies are responsible for informing growers of the EPA rules and are required to instruct the growers in the planting and care of refuges. To obtain seeds produced by biotechnology, growers have been required since 2002 to sign an insect resistance management agreement. However, even with these regulations, there is still a lot of miscommunication, misunderstanding, and noncompliance.

Suggested Answers for Case Analysis

1. **Recognize potential issues and major topics in the case.** What is this case about? Underline terms or phrases that seem to be important to understanding this case. Then list **3 or 4** biology-related topics or issues in the case.

   Biology-related topics or issues: spread of genes from one variety of corn to another via pollen, how Bt corn is produced, reasons for its production, refuges for preserving the effectiveness of pesticide genes, planting Bt corn versus non-Bt corn.

2. **What specific questions do you have about these topics?** By yourself, or better yet, in a group, make a list of what you already know about this case in the "What Do I Know?" column. List questions you would like to learn more about in the "What Do I Need to Know?" column.

   There are many possible answers, depending on the experience of your students. Some likely responses follow.

What Do I Know?	What Do I Need to Know?
• *Familiarity with corn—sweet and popcorn— as well as husking corn and picking off the silks.* • *Some students may be familiar with application of pesticides.* • *Chemicals are often used to control insects.* • *Bt can affect butterfly larvae.* • *Some people may be allergic to Bt corn.* • *Some students may be more familiar with cultivation practices than other students.* • *Some students may have studied GM crops in some detail and have info to share on benefits, potential problems, and methods of producing these crops.*	• *What is Bt corn?* • *Is Bt corn widely grown?* • *What is tasseling?* • *What is pollen drift?* • *What is volunteer corn?* • *What is a refuge? How is it planted?* • *What are differences in cultivation methods of Bt and other types of corn?* • *Why do the affected growers now have to sell their corn as feed?* • *Do humans eat Bt corn?* • *Are European corn borers endangered?* • *What kinds of damage do the corn borers* • *What kinds of damage do the corn borers do to the plants?* • *What are the benefits of GM crops?*

3. Put a check mark by **1–3** questions or issues from the "What Do I Need to Know?" list that you think are most important to explore.

   You should expect a range of responses, but most students will use the contextual clues of being in a biology class and beginning the plant structure and function unit.

4. **What kinds of references or resources would help you answer or explore these questions?** Identify two different resources and explain what information each resource is likely to give that will help you answer the question(s). Choose specific resources.

Accept any reasonable resource (e.g., text, other book, Internet sites, data tables, and so on) that could be related to the case. The answer "the Web" is too vague. Students should explain the type of site they are looking for or search terms they might use.

Suggested Answers for Core Investigations

I. Critical Reading

To complete this investigation, you should have already read Chapter 38: Angiosperm Reproduction and Biotechnology.

A. Reproduction in Corn: Flowers and Pollination. Like the majority of angiosperms, rose family plants have complete flowers. Their floral structure includes sepals, petals, stamens, and carpels (Figure 6.2). If you compare corn flowers to the rose flower, you can observe striking differences. Corn, known globally as *maize*, has unisexual flowers and is monoecious—both male (staminate) and female (carpellate) flowers are found on the same plant. The staminate flowers are located in the tassels produced at the top of the plant. The carpellate flowers are produced in rows on upright ears found lower on the cornstalk.

Figure 6.2 Complete flowers such as this *Rosa* species have both male and female reproductive parts. Maize flowers, however, contain either male or female reproductive parts.

1. Is there any advantage for the corn plant to having its staminate flowers higher than its carpellate flowers? Explain.

   The pollen can be more easily dispersed by the wind, and pollen will fall onto the lower carpellate flowers even without much wind to disperse the pollen.

2. Each tassel produces 2–5 million pollen grains. One acre of a cornfield may contain 20,000 to 30,000 corn plants, producing up to 68 kg (approximately 150 pounds) of pollen in a single growing season. Each ear has about 1,000 carpellate flowers, although only about 400 seed-containing kernels are produced on the average ear.

The pollents ovule ratio (P/O) in wind-pollinated plants is often greater than 1,000 (1,000 pollen grains:1 ovule). For example, horse chestnut has a P/O of 450,000 and oak has a P/O of 600,000. If 4 million grains of pollen are produced per tassel, what is the ratio of pollen to ovules in an average corn plant bearing one tassel and one ear?

4,000,000/1,000 = 4,000

3. Pollen grain size is significant (see Figure 6.3). If a pollen grain is too large, it may not disperse well; however, if it is too small, there will be insufficient resources to produce a pollen tube long enough to reach the ovules. Corn pollen averages 120 μm in diameter, which is much larger than either horse chestnut or oak pollen. Unlike either of these tree pollens, corn has to support the growth of a pollen tube up to 15 cm long.

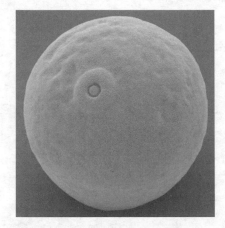

Figure 6.3 A corn pollen grain (~90 μm).

Western ragweed pollen averages 21 μm in diameter and produces a pollen tube length of about 1 cm. Consider the differences in pollen production by corn (4 million grains per plant) and western ragweed (75 million pollen grains per plant). (Western ragweed pollen per stem was calculated from data presented in Wan et al., 2000, Response of an allergenic species, *Ambrosia psilostachya* (asteraceae), to experimental warming and clipping: Implications for public health. *American Journal of Botany* 89(11): 1843–1846.) Speculate how the characteristics of each plant's pollen benefit the reproduction of its species.

Corn pollen requires more nutrients to support the growth of pollen tubes that are up to 15 times longer than those in ragweed. While both plants are wind-pollinated, the western ragweed pollen is 5 to 6 times smaller and lighter, allowing it to be dispersed more readily. This is a benefit to a species where individuals may grow far apart from each other. The western ragweed also produces 15 to 35 times more pollen per plant, thus increasing the pollen's likelihood of traveling a greater distance.

4. If you didn't know that corn is wind-pollinated, what characteristics of corn flowers could point you toward this conclusion?

Accept any reasonable explanation. The flowers lack petals. Carpellate flowers produce long, sticky silks that extend out of the ear. Staminate flowers are produced at the very top of the plant, enabling wind dissemination.

5. How do you think a rose is pollinated? Consider your own experience with roses as well as the image provided in Figure 6.2. List two personal observations to support your answer.

   The rose is likely to be pollinated by insects or other animals. The rose has brightly colored petals, is usually fragrant, and is often observed with insects on the flower.

6. Roses belong to the clade of flowering plants called eudicots. Corn belongs to the monocot clade. Using your knowledge of eudicot and monocot traits, answer "monocot" or "eudicot" for the following features observed in plants from one of these two clades:

   a. Parallel venation in the leaves

      monocot

   b. Vascular bundles in the stem arranged in a ring

      eudicot

   c. The seedling produces a single cotyledon

      monocot

B. Reproduction: Fertilization and the Seed. See Figures 38.3 and 38.8 in the text to help you with this investigation.

1. If you were to slice open a kernel of corn and apply iodine solution to the interior, which part of the kernel do you predict would turn the darkest blue? What is the function of this part of the seed?

   Most likely the endosperm would turn the darkest blue because it contains the highest concentration of starch. The endosperm provides nutrients to the embryo (during germination) until the plant can perform photosynthesis.

2. Do the embryo and endosperm contain genetic information from the female gamete, the male gamete, or both?

   Both the embryo and the endosperm contain genetic information from both types of gametes. One sperm fertilizes the egg, forming a zygote. The second sperm combines with the two polar nuclei in an egg cell to form a triploid (3n) nucleus in the center of the large central cell of the embryo sac. This large cell gives rise to the endosperm.

3. Do both the embryo and the endosperm have the same number of chromosomes? Explain.

   No. The embryo has fewer chromosomes. One sperm nucleus fertilizes the egg cell, forming a diploid zygote (2n). The other sperm nucleus fertilizes the polar body nuclei to form a triploid endosperm (3n). The zygote and endosperm undergo mitosis, resulting in an embryo and ample endosperm to support the embryo through germination.

II. Considering *Bt* Corn

A. Misplaced *Bt* Corn. Recall from the case that something strange happened in Macon County. Some of the corn stored in the major grain elevator tested positive for new *Bt* genes. These genes are found in some kinds of genetically modified corn, but this corn was not planted in Macon County according to the cooperative records. (*Note:* Macon County shares some of its north and west borders with DeWitt County.)

1. List the hypotheses posed by the DeWitt County growers as to how new *Bt* corn found its way into the Macon County growers' grain elevators.

   John—pollen drift; Sam—volunteer corn; Emmet—seed company mix-up

2. Consider how the *Bt* genes turned up in the Macon County corn according to John's hypothesis. Within the seeds, would *Bt* genes be found in the embryo, the endosperm, or both? Explain.

   Corn pollen from Bt *corn grown in DeWitt County was carried by the wind to cornfields in nearby Macon County. (Note: Pollen drift usually does not exceed half a mile.) The pollen nuclei would contribute* Bt *genes to both the endosperm and the embryo of the non-*Bt *corn during fertilization.*

3. Farms are spread out all around Macon County. Two members of the growers' cooperative had samples of seed from corn left in their fields that tested for the presence of *Bt* genes. Compare the test results of field A and field B in Figure 6.4.

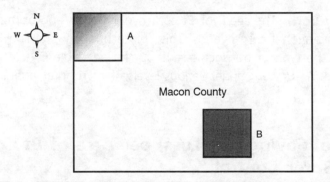

Figure 6.4 Two fields with *Bt* test results in Macon County. Gray indicates the presence of *Bt* genes in the field. The more corn that tested positive for *Bt* genes, the darker the gray scale.

   Field A shows a graduated occurrence of Bt genes. The field B location tests uniformly positive for Bt genes.

4. Which field results would tend to support John's explanation of how pollen traveled from DeWitt to Macon County? Why?

   Field A. The gradation seems to indicate that the source is west-northwest, and we know that the wind comes from the west-northwest where DeWitt growers raise this kind of Bt *corn.*

5. Which field results would tend to support Emmet's explanation? Why?

   Field B supports a seed mix-up. Plants with the genes are uniformly present throughout the field and are unlikely to be due to either pollen drift or volunteer corn (grows from unharvested seeds left behind the prior year).

6. Draw a new rectangle to represent field C with results that would support Sam's hypothesis. Explain the significance of the pattern of *Bt* genes in your sketch.

Example of a student sketch:

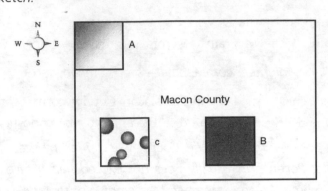

Figure IG6.1 *Answer to student Figure 6.4*

The Bt *genes are found in random areas within the field where volunteer corn occasionally germinates successfully.*

B. The Economics of *Bt* Corn. The seed for *Bt* corn hybrids costs approximately $14 more per bag than the seed for conventional corn hybrids. This "biotechnology premium" varies from year to year and depends on the type of transgenic seed purchased. Table 6.1 describes the potential savings (or losses) of using *Bt* corn under various levels of corn borer populations and corn pricing.

Table 6.1 Potential Savings (or Loss) per Acre of *Bt* Corn Versus No Corn Borer Control.[1]

Average Number of Borers/Plant[2]	Corn Price per Bushel			
	$1.50	**$2.00**	**$2.50**	**$3.00**
0.00	($4.55)	($4.55)	($4.55)	($4.55)
0.25	($1.99)	($1.13)	($0.27)	$0.58
0.50	$0.58	$2.29	$4.00	$5.71
1.00	$5.71	$9.13	$12.55	$15.97
1.50	$10.84	$15.97	$21.10	$26.23
2.00	$15.97	$22.81	$29.65	$36.49

[1]This table assumes: a yield potential of 144 bushel per acre; *Bt* corn costs $14 extra per bag; a seeding rate of 26,000/acre.

[2]The number of corn borers that would complete development in a non-*Bt* hybrid.

1. Estimate the net loss or net gain for a farmer with 2,000 acres in the following scenarios:

   a. Corn prices are low ($1.50) and so are the corn borer populations (about 1 for every 4 corn plants, or 0.25).

      number of acres × number of bushels × table value of corn

      2,000 × 144 × −$1.99 = −$573,120.00 (loss)

   b. Corn prices are high ($2.50) and so are the corn borer population sizes (about 1 for every plant, or 1.00).

      number of acres × number of bushels × table value of corn

      2,000 × 144 × $12.55 = $3,614,400.00 (gain)

2. What other factors might enter into a grower's decision about whether to plant *Bt* corn?

   The severity of corn borers in the area and seasonal forecasts. The number of expected generations of ECB for the region. The marketability of genetically modified corn. The size of the farm—if large enough to make planting the required refuges feasible. If the farmer wants to grow organic corn, then Bt corn is not an option. The kind of corn being grown, whether for animal feed or for human consumption, is another factor. Some students may mention that Bt *corn is easier to manage than* Bt *sprays. The transgenic corn does not need to be checked on a weekly basis.*

C. Simulations: Hybridization and Genetic Engineering of Crops.

1. *Bt* corn is made by replicating the gene for the *Bt* toxin found in the bacterium *Bacillus thuringiensis* and inserting the gene into corn. Techniques described in Chapter 20 enable the plant engineer to identify plants that have incorporated the *Bt* gene. Go to the Case Book website to run a simulation for engineering transgenic tomatoes.

   Have students print out and submit the final Web page of the simulation so that you know they completed the assignment.

2. Figure 38.16 in the text compares modern corn with its ancestral plant, teosinte. Neolithic farmers selected for traits such as large cobs and kernel size as well as a tough husk encasing the entire cob. Over time, this artificial selection led to the development of modern maize. Go to the Case Book website to use a selective breeding simulation for engineering bigger, better corn.

   Have students print out and submit the final Web page of the simulation so that you know they completed the assignment.

3. Although both of these strategies are examples of artificial selection of crop plants, describe two differences between these approaches.

   Among the answers might be the following: Hybridization has been used for thousands of years, but genetic engineering is new. It takes many generations to produce plants with the gene combination you desire, but it can be done through genetic engineering within one generation. Hybridization uses only the genes that naturally occur in corn (including mutations) and genetic engineering uses genes outside of corn. Hybridization can be low-tech (though often it is not), while genetic engineering requires high-tech labs and procedures.

D. Alternatives for Controlling European Corn Borers. The European corn borer (ECB) was introduced into the United States in the early 1900s, most likely arriving with imported European plant
products. Without predators to keep the population in check, ECBs spread rapidly. In most of the
United States, this moth produces multiple generations in a single year. Various environmental factors influence the population sizes from year to year. Isolating infested fields and burning the plant
material was the only method of control until the mid-1920s (Figure 6.5) when the bacterium
Bacillus thuringiensis was discovered to have pesticidal properties. By 1930, growers were spraying
their crops with a mixture containing live *B. thuringiensis,* which was effective against ECBs for as
long as the pesticide-producing bacteria survived—several days at most. Although chemical pesticides became widely available after World War II, the majority of growers continued to use the *B.
thuringiensis* mixture.

1. Many farmers growing corn using conventional methods still choose to apply *B. thuringiensis* sprays.
What are the advantages of this strategy for controlling ECBs?

   *The farmers use the bacterial mixture because it works well, is not harmful to their health, and does
   not persist for more than a few days. If used when the ECB population is still in its early stage, it can be
   effective in controlling ECB. (Note: Bt corn is still the most effective because the plants produce the Bt
   protein continuously.) The nontransgenic corn seed is less expensive than the Bt seed. Markets requiring nontransgenic crops would be open to these farmers. Organic farmers can use this spray because
   it is "natural" and they make more money per bushel of corn that is sold for human consumption.*

2. What are some of the disadvantages of applying sprays?

   *The effects of direct bacterial applications are short-lived. In some locations, several applications may
   be required each growing season. This method requires that someone walk in the fields to look for evidence of ECB damage throughout the season. The development of resistance to Bt spray is still possible, although not as likely as in transgenic Bt cornfields. Other ideas might include: Application of the
   spray may be difficult in a mature, crowded cornfield; and overspraying of Bt is likely, especially if it is
   windy.*

III. Investigating Corn Morphology and Growth with a Model of Insect Damage

A. Corn Morphology. Maize is a member of the grass family. As you may recall from Chapter 35,
grasses contain meristematic tissue in each node along the length of their shoots as well as in a
basal meristem. Although most other plants produce new growth from apical meristems, grass
leaves and shoots grow up from the base. Mowing is the equivalent of a "haircut" for grasses,
which grow back quickly. Nongrass plants recover from mowing much more slowly, because new
apical meristems must form.

1. How does this type of growth in the leaves help grasses survive being eaten by herbivores such
as bison?

   *Browsers such as bison would substantially slow the regrowth of grasses if they ate growing tips (meris-
   tems) rather than the older tips of the leaves. Because new leaves are produced from the base, they
   continue to emerge even after the tops are nibbled. Elongation of the stem and leaves occurs along the
   entire shoot, allowing the nibbled leaves to continue elongating.*

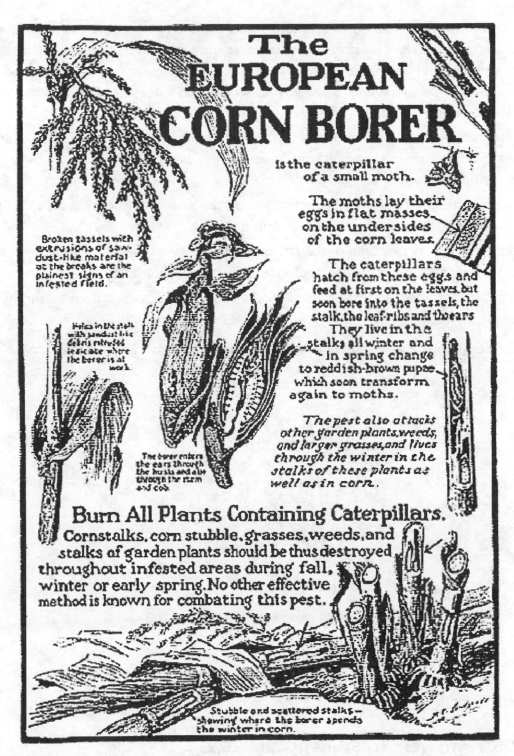

Figure 6.5 In 1919, the only method of controlling corn borers was crop destruction.

2. When corn is infested with ECBs, several types of damage can occur. Late-season borers may invade the corn ears. Not only does this result in an unsightly appearance and decrease in yield, but the damaged sites are also likely to be colonized by bacteria and fungi. Production of toxic by-products from certain species of fungi such as aflatoxin can result in the entire crop being rejected at the mill.

Another kind of damage occurs when ECBs tunnel into the solid stalks and create hollow spaces that weaken the plant, which may collapse. Like the damaged ears, damaged stems are also inviting to bacteria and fungi.

Considering what you have learned about stem structure and function, describe an additional problem that is likely to result from ECBs stem tunneling.

To get a better understanding of the structure and growth of grasses like corn, we will study yet a different type of damage from the ECB, called "shot holes."

The tunnels disrupt xylem and phloem tissues. The conduction of sufficient water and nutrients is threatened.

3. Using Figure 6.6, note the position of each leaf and fill in Table 6.2. Row D is filled in for you.

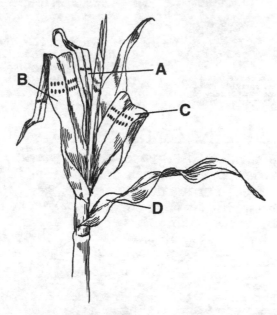

Figure 6.6 A corn plant with early season damage from European corn borers.

Table IG6.3 Answers to Student Table 6.2.

Leaf	Damage	Comparative Age
A	*One row of holes*	*Youngest*
B	*Two rows of holes*	Older than A
C	*Two rows of holes*	Older than A and B
D	None observed	Older than A, B, and C

When the ECB caterpillars first emerge, corn is in an early stage of growth that farmers describe as the *whorl* stage. The new leaves are tightly wrapped around each other at first. Then, as the stem elongates, they separate. The leaves dramatically expand as their cells mature and elongate.

4. Do you think that the damage in Figure 6.6 was caused by several caterpillars feeding on the leaves successively or by one or two feeding at the same time? Explain.

   This is just to prompt students to propose an explanation. Although the second explanation better describes the phenomenon, either hypothesis could be supported by students.

   a. *Several caterpillars feeding successively—lots of holes on different leaves.*

   b. *One or two feeding at the same time—holes are in rows, as if caused by tunneling. The subsequent elongation of leaves causes this to look like the result of independent events.*

B. Making a Model of Shot Hole Damage to Explore Growth. Models are often useful in exploring complex phenomena by limiting the number of factors involved. Models allow us to simulate interactions, test hypotheses, and ask new questions.

To examine the cause of shot hole damage, you need to first construct a physical model of a young corn plant in whorl stage with three leaves. Then use this model to simulate the feeding activity of corn borers. You need a sheet of ruled notebook paper (8½" × 11"), a ruler, scissors, a writing instrument, and a straight pin.

Part 1: Making the Leaves

Step 1: With the pen or pencil, draw a vertical line at 4 inches and another at 7 inches from the left edge of the paper (Figure 6.7a).

Step 2: Cut the paper lengthwise along the two lines you have drawn so that you have three vertical strips to represent three leaves (Figure 6.7b).

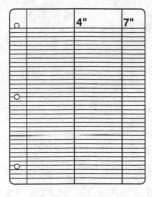

Figure 6.7a

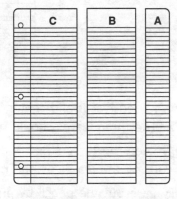

Figure 6.7b

Step 3: Mark the top of the thinnest strip as leaf A, the next widest as leaf B, and the widest as leaf C.

Part 2: Modeling the Age of the Leaves

Step 1: Mark leaf A 10 lines from the bottom (Figure 6.7c). Roll the strip tightly from the bottom until you reach the 10-line mark. Press firmly to fold the rolled paper in place. Leaf A is the youngest leaf. It is the thinnest and the shortest. Much of its maturation and elongation has not occurred.

Step 2: Mark leaf B at 5 lines from the bottom. Repeat the roll-and-fold process from step 1. Leaf B is the middle leaf and should be longer and wider than leaf A.

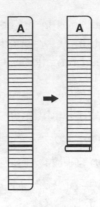

Figure 6.7c

Step 3: Leaf C does not require folding. Leaf C is the oldest leaf and should be the widest and longest. It has completed most of its maturation and elongation.

Part 3: Assembling the Whorl

Step 1: Mark leaf C in the center of the strip 5 lines from the bottom. Label this mark "node 1." Mark leaf B in the center of the strip at 5 lines from the bottom. Label this mark "node 2" (Figure 6.7d).

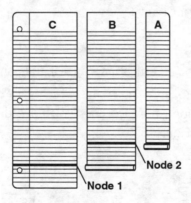

Figure 6.7d

Step 2: Take the folded leaf B and center its base on node 1. Take the folded leaf A and center its base on node 2. The three leaves should now be stacked (Figure 6.7e).

Step 3: Carefully keep the three strips in place (you could use a small piece of tape to secure leaf B and leaf A) as you roll the leaves as one unit from the side around your writing instrument.

Step 4: Carefully ease out the pencil by pulling it from the center while firmly holding the strips. Then flatten the roll of strips lengthwise for easier handling.

Part 4: Simulating the Corn Borer Damage

Step 1: The resulting model of a corn plant whorl should look tubelike. If you feel along the tube, there will be a noticeable thickening where leaf B begins and another where leaf A begins. These represent nodes on the stem, where the meristems that produce the leaves are located.

Step 2: Locate the flattened area between the node for leaf B and the node for leaf A 2.5 inches or so from the bottom. Take the pin and push it once through the whorl at this location. This simulates the path a borer makes while eating, or "boring," its way straight through the leaves.

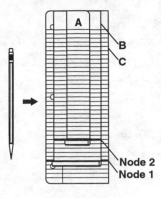

Figure 6.7e

Step 3: Locate the flattened area above the node for leaf A 3.5 inches or so from the bottom. Take the pin and push it once through the whorl at this location. This simulates a new path the same borer or a second borer makes while eating its way straight through the leaves.

Part 5: Modeling Growth After the Damage

Step 1: Unroll the model of the damaged whorl and separate leaf A from leaf B and leaf B from leaf C.

Step 2: Unroll the shortened strips of leaf A and leaf B. Carefully replace or reattach the bottom of the unrolled leaves to the nodes that they were attached to before you unrolled them. This repositioning of the leaves models the elongation of both the stem and the leaves during normal growth.

1. Describe the pattern of damage you see on the leaves by filling in Table 6.3.

   Hint: You could ask students to bring in their final models for demonstration. This could be evaluated if desired.

Table IG6.4 Answers to Student Table 6.3.

Leaf	Damage
A	*One row of holes*
B	*Two rows of holes*
C	*Two rows of holes*

2. Look again at Figure 6.6 of shot hole damage. Are your model results consistent with this picture?

   Yes. The results in Table 6.2 for leaves A, B, and C are identical and match those in Table 6.1 as well as those observed in the figure.

3. What do you consider to be the limitations of this model of corn growth?

   There is no real stem, the leaves don't expand in width, the borers might make different numbers of holes, and you don't have a sense of how long it takes for the whorl to unfurl. Corn leaves are not "rolled up" at the bottom and do not "unroll" as they grow.

4. What do you consider to be the strengths of this model of corn growth?

We get a hands-on model that demonstrates meristems and leaf growth. The simulation closely matches the damage done by corn borers in the field, so perhaps it is a good model for some aspects of how corn plants grow. It only requires paper, pencil, and scissors, which makes it simple to construct.

5. Do you think making a physical model was helpful in understanding this pattern of damage by European corn borers? Explain.

Yes. The model provided a plausible explanation for how the pattern of damage could be generated as the leaves grow.

  If no, then look for an adequate explanation.

IV. Refuges for Resistance Management

In the case, we saw that the farmers were going to discuss planting refuges for the European corn borer (ECB). The Environmental Protection Agency requires every grower who plants *Bt* corn to use a refuge so that some *Bt*-susceptible corn borers will survive. When *Bt*-susceptible corn borer moths mature, they are available in adequate numbers to mate with any rare *Bt*-resistant corn borer moth that survives in the *Bt* corn. The eggs produced from these matings are more likely to contain embryos that possess susceptibility genes to *Bt* toxin. In this way, refuges help maintain the gene frequencies for susceptibility in the ECB population and overcome the *Bt*-resistance selection effects found in the *Bt* cornfields. While resistant populations of ECB are quite likely to develop in the future, the purpose of the refuges is to slow this process. (*Note:* You may wish to use the Hardy-Weinberg equilibrium model to look at the effect of migration on gene frequencies to justify the refuge concept. See the Investigation on the Campbell website in Chapter 23, *How Can Frequency of Alleles Be Calculated?*)

1. In the case, the growers meet to discuss planting refuges in order to reduce the chance that a population of corn borers resistant to *Bt* toxin will become established. Offer two explanations why the development of resistant bacteria is more difficult to control than the development of resistant corn borers. (*Hint:* See the heading "R Plasmids and Antibiotic Resistance" in Concept 27.2.)

Accept any reasonable explanation, including:

- *Population size and reproduction play a significant role in the spread of resistance. Once bacteria gain resistance by mutation or the exchange of plasmids, asexual reproduction and short reproductive cycles quickly lead to populations of resistant bacteria. Resistant corn borers must mate to pass the trait to their offspring. Sexual reproduction by resistant individuals is the only way to increase the number of Bt-resistant ECBs in the population.*

- *Bacteria are everywhere and may encounter antibiotics in many locations. Corn borers encounter the Bt toxin in managed fields in which strategies such as refuges or intermittent Bt sprays are actively used.*

- *Prevention of the evolution of resistance in ECBs is easier than prevention of the evolution of antibiotic resistance in bacteria because we can use strategies such as refuges with corn populations. With humans we would not refuse to administer antibiotics if we thought they were needed.*

2. All the refuge plans shown in Figure 6.8 provide an interface between *Bt* and non-*Bt* corn. Do you think the block refuge or the split planter refuge would be more likely to facilitate the opportunity for a rare *Bt*-resistant corn borer moth to mate with a moth that isn't *Bt*-resistant? Explain.

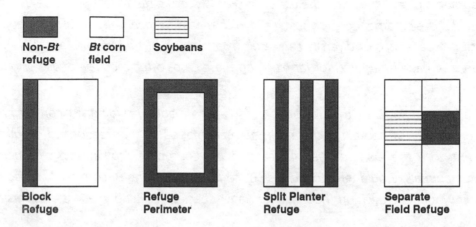

Figure 6.8 Several options for planting refuges. Federal guidelines call for refuges to constitute at least 20% of field space.

The split planter refuge provides more access opportunities between moths emerging from Bt corn and non-Bt corn. The interspersing of the two kinds of plants provides more contact between potentially resistant and nonresistant moths due to a greater length of adjacency.

Suggested Answers for Additional Investigation

V. Making Decisions About DNA Technology: Golden Rice

1. Complete the Web/CD Activity: Making Decisions About DNA Technology in Chapter 38. This activity raises a concern that transgenic crops may reduce biodiversity. In your own words, explain how this might occur and why it is significant.

Transgenic crops may prove to be so successful that not planting them would result in economic loss. Farmers choosing traditional crops would lose the ability to compete in the market. As more farms replace traditional crops with the new transgenic crop, diversity is lost. The shift to monoculture invites increased risk for disease and the loss of valuable diverse traits that may offer solutions to future problems.

2. Consider your explanation above. Do these risks only apply to transgenic seeds, or is this also true of the hybrid seed that farmers have been using for many years?

This is true for both.

3. In developing nations, farmers generally depend on crops that produce both food and seed. Develop arguments both for and against the distribution of *Bt* corn seed to farmers in developing nations. Is a growing reliance on seed companies problematic, or do the benefits outweigh the risks?

Before you answer this question, consider reading the following two position papers from *Action Bioscience* on the Case Book website:

"The Ecological Impacts of Agricultural Biotechnology" by Miguel A. Altieri, February 2001.

"Biotechnology and the Green Revolution," interview with Norman Borlaug, November 2002.

Several arguments can be made for the use of Bt *corn:* Bt *corn requires less pesticide use; the use of* Bt *corn can yield more corn per acre (or hectare), which means farmers will be able to feed more people using the same space; loss of diversity can result from the use of traditional crops with poorer yields, because more acreage is required for farming and these crops often require the use of both pesticides and fertilizers.*

Several arguments against the use of Bt *corn can be made, including:* Bt *corn might prove too expensive or too hard to obtain each season; farmers may value the freedom to produce their own seed to plant corn the next year; an increase in the consumer populations, whether humans or domesticated animals, would tend to increase* Bt *corn plantings, and* Bt *corn could be so profitable as a crop that it would encroach on the space for native species, resulting in a loss of diversity.*

VI. Open-Ended Investigations

A gene from Antarctic fish that allows the fish to avoid freezing has been put into tomatoes. These tomatoes also survive hard frost.

Find another gene that might be valuable for either crop management, enhanced growth, or nutritional quality and tell why. Identifiy the source of the genes and the target crop.

Chapter 7:

Galloper's Gut

INSTRUCTOR'S GUIDE

As with all the cases in this book, please read the preface if you have not already done so. In the preface you will find suggestions for using Investigative Case–Based Learning (ICBL) in different instructional situations such as starting a new lecture topic, assessing what students already know, setting a context for lab activities, and so on. The preface also describes ways to use cases in a variety of classroom settings, and suggests multiple ways to assess learning with cases.

Galloper's Gut accompanies Unit Seven: Animal Form and Function in Campbell and Reece's *Biology*, 8th edition. The case, in which a new employee learns about feeding horses, emphasizes material in Chapter 41: Animal Nutrition. There are four strands in the case:

- Structure and function of selected mammalian digestive systems

- Nutrition for horses

- Issues in reproduction

- Horse evolution

Students should complete the Case Analysis immediately following the reading of the case. We strongly suggest that students work in groups to complete the Case Analysis. Actively listening to and challenging the ideas of others can help learners become aware of their own misconceptions, yet also value their own and others' prior knowledge.

Four investigations accompany *Galloper's Gut*. Two are "core" investigations relating directly to the facts of the case, and two are additional investigations that use Web-based resources or extend beyond the science referred to in the case itself. Table IG7.1 explains what students will gain from each investigation.

Table IG7.1 Galloper's Gut Case Overview.

Investigation	Learning Goals	Inquiry Skills Used
Core Investigations		
I. Critical Reading	Students learn about digestive system structure and function in different types of mammals. Emphasis is on postgastric fermenters (horses and humans) and ruminants.	• observation • inference
II. Feeding Horses	Students investigate nutritional requirements and implications of improper diet, along with pasture problems. They analyze a spreadsheet to examine appropriate mixtures of feed for different conditions.	• analyzing data • relating structure to function
Additional Investigations		
III. Reproduction in Mammals	Students create graphs with their own collected data related to gestation periods. They evaluate whether two species that can produce hybrids should be considered the same species.	• generating hypotheses • consideration of data to collect • displaying data graphically
IV. A Closer Look at Horse Evolution	Students examine trends in jaw, diet, and foot adaptations.	• observation • inference
V. Open-Ended Investigations	Students may use a live Excel model on the Case Book website to explore nutritional needs of horses' various characteristics.	• manipulating variables in a model

Table IG7.2 contains several resources related to *Biology*, 8th edition, that will help your students further their understanding of this case. Note that chapter readings and activities are listed in order of importance.

Table IG7.2 Campbell-Related Resources.

Resource	Chapter/Activity	Topics Covered/Activity Title
Critical Reading from *Biology*, 8th edition	Chapter 41: Animal Nutrition	Animal dietary categories (Overview); Figure 41.2: Four main feeding mechanisms of animals; Figure 41.3: Homeostatic regulation of cellular fuel (Concept 41.1); main stages of food processing (Concept 41.3); the mammalian digestive system; Figure 41.15: The human digestive system (Concept 41.4); evolutionary adaptations of vertebrate digestive systems; Figure 41.28: Ruminant digestion (Concept 41.5)
Related Readings	Chapter 24: The Origin of Species	Anagenesis and cladogenesis (Overview); biological species concept; reproductive isolation (Concept 24.1); Figure 25.25: The branched evolution of horses (Concept 25.6)
Campbell website/ CD-ROM	Chapter 41 **Investigation**	What Role Does Amylase Play in Digestion?
	Chapter 41 **Activity**	Digestive System Function
	Chapter 24 **Investigation**	How Do New Species Arise by Geographic Isolation?

Case Narrative

Students were asked to underline terms or phrases in the introductory narrative that they think are important to understanding the case. Suggested terms and phrases that students might have chosen are in bold type.

As she walked into the **horse** barn with Jim and Gina, Leah smiled to herself. Not only did she have a summer job working with horses, but she would get time on horseback as well.

Gina explained, "We have four horses right now. The **mare and her foal,** a **three-year-old stallion we are training** for competition, and this little **yearling that is just not growing** very well. We have to keep him in the barn all the time to **control his feed.**"

"The grass here is not like the grass we had in Kentucky," Jim declared. "We have to **give the horses extra minerals.**"

"The soil in the pasture is a problem," Gina agreed. "But we are **replanting with both alfalfa and timothy.** Among other things, the local **fescue grass turned out to be infected with a fungus.** It may be the problem with our little guy, though."

Leah looked around the barn, trying to take it all in. "I didn't get to feed horses before" she said. "What do I do?"

"You'll need to learn to **prepare the supplemental feed** and give it to each horse **twice a** day," Jim replied. "We'll show you what to do."

Leah noticed the feeding plan posted on the wall near the bins of feed. "Gosh," she said, "I had no idea it was so complicated. I thought all horses just grazed in the pasture and maybe had oats for a treat. But **each of your horses gets a different feed** mixture and in different amounts."

"That's right. **Each animal has different needs depending on its size and level of activity,**" Jim said. "For example, we're training Best Boy so he gets a heavy workout every day. He's an **easy keeper,** but he does better with some extra oats because of his high activity level."

Gina added, "The mare is **lactating now, so she is on a different ratio of hay, grain,** and supplements than the others."

"So, do the horses need to go out to the pasture to feed at all?" Leah asked.

"Yes, unless you leave a lot of **good-quality hay** for them to get at in the barn," Gina explained.

"Hay should be **green and contain more leaves than stems.** The stems should be flexible. Another way I can tell if hay is good is to check if the bale is easy to lift. Heavy bales usually contain water and that might mean mold."

"Horses actually have a very **small stomach for their size,** so they have to eat almost **constantly,**" Jim explained. "Because of this intense grazing, each horse needs about **two acres of pastureland** to support it. **Bad things happen** when **too many grazing animals are kept on too little land.**"

"Like that guy down the road with the buffalo?" Leah asked.

"Yes. He has too many animals in that space. His buffalo are definitely too small, and I'd bet they need to be **wormed,**" Gina answered.

"Hey, let's get started with the yearling before we try to solve the buffalo problem," Jim said.

Suggested Answers for Case Analysis

1. **Recognize potential issues and major topics in the case.** What is this case about? Underline terms or phrases that seem to be important to understanding this case. Then list **3 or 4** biology-related topics or issues in the case.

   Biology-related topics or issues: horse feeding and digestion, overcrowding of grazing animals, diseases, reproduction, growth

2. **What specific questions do you have about these topics?** By yourself, or better yet, in a group, make a list of what you already know about this case in the "What Do I Know?" column. List questions you would like to learn more about in the "What Do I Need to Know?" column.

There are many possible answers, depending on the experience of your students. Some likely responses follow.

What Do I Know?	What Do I Need to Know?
• *Horses graze in pastures and eat hay.* • *Horses were brought here by the Spanish in the 1500s. (Note: While this is so, horses actually originally evolved in what became North America, then spread out to South America, Europe, Asia, and Africa. It is thought that North American horses became extinct around 8000 BC from a combination of factors including overhunting.)* • *Some horses are domesticated and some are wild.* • *Horses live in herds of females with a single stallion.* • *You can tell the age of a horse by looking at its teeth. (Note: Actually, this is less accurate than generally believed and depends on the breed of the horse and whether it has been stabled or not.)* • *Students who own or ride horses will have much more to add.*	• *What is the fungus in the fescue? Does it affect horses?* • *What is supplemental feed?* • *What minerals does a horse need? Why?* • *Why do different horses need different nutritional supplements?* • *How do horses digest hay and oats?* • *How can an animal live on hay?* • *Where did horses come from originally?* • *What else could be wrong with the yearling?* • *How long are mares pregnant?* • *How long do foals nurse?* • *Why replant with both alfalfa and timothy?* • *How does lactation affect nutritional requirements?* • *How do horse nutritional requirements compare to our own? To other mammals'?* • *How does crowding affect animal health?*

3. Put a check mark by **1–3** questions or issues from the "What Do I Need to Know?" list that you think are most important to explore.

   You should expect a range of responses. Most students will use the contextual clues of being in a biology class and beginning the animal physiology unit to identify animal form and function questions.

4. **What kinds of references or resources would help you answer or explore these questions?** Identify two different resources and explain what information each resource is likely to give that will help you answer the question(s). Choose specific resources.

   Accept any reasonable resource (e.g., text, other book, Internet sites, maps, data tables, and so on) that could be related to this case. The answer "the Web" is too vague. Students should explain the type of site they are looking for or search terms they might use.

Suggested Answers for Core Investigations

I. Critical Reading

Before beginning the investigations, read Chapter 41: Animal Nutrition in your text. You may also have to refer to other chapters in Unit Seven and Chapter 24: The Origin of Species to learn the most from this investigative case.

1. Compare the digestive systems of cattle (in this instance a cow), horses, and humans using Figure 7.2, as well as Figures 41.28 and 41.15 in your text.

   a. How does the structure of the stomach in these three organisms differ?

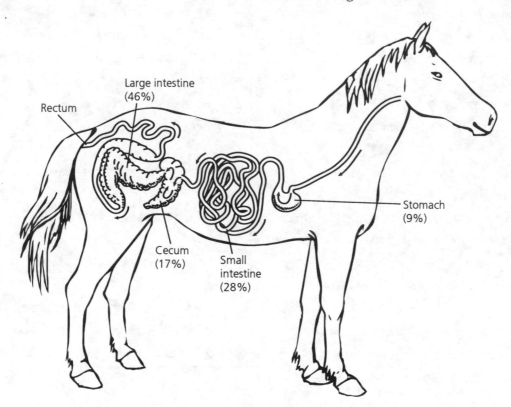

Figure 7.2 Idealized digestive system of the horse—a postgastric fermenter. The percentages refer to the relative capacities of each structure.

   The cow has a four-chambered stomach that includes the rumen, reticulum, omasum, and aboma-sum. Horses and humans have a single-chambered stomach.

   b. Examine Figure 7.3. Note the significant difference in the relative capacity of the stomach when comparing a horse with a cow. What do you think this indicates about the location of digestion in both animals?

   In cows, almost all digestion occurs in the stomach, where large populations of microbes thrive. Because the stomach of the horse is so small in comparison to the cow, much more digestion must occur after the food has left the stomach.

   c. How do you think the relative capacities of the stomach, small intestine, and large intestine would differ in humans as compared to horses and cows?

   In humans, the stomach, small intestine, and large intestine have about the same capacity.

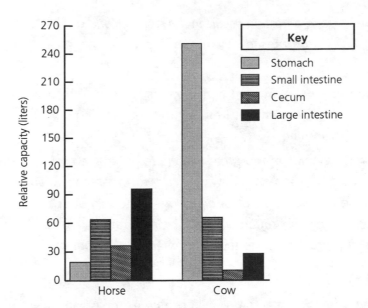

Figure 7.3 Relative capacities of the digestive tracts in horses and cows. (Adapted from: Ensminger and Olentine, 1978)

2. Where are the microbes (mostly facultatively anaerobic) involved in digestion primarily located in the cow, horse, and human?

   In cows, most of the digestive microbes live in two of the stomach chambers, the rumen and the reticulum (cows are known as gastric fermenters). A small cecum found in cows also contains fermenting microbes. Horses have a large cecum where the small and large intestines connect. The digestive microbes found in horses are primarily located in the cecum and large intestine; there are no stomach compartments with microbes. Humans also have a cecum connecting the small intestine with the large intestine. Both the size and function of the human cecum are very reduced compared with other mammals. (The human appendix, a lymphatic organ, is an extension of the cecum.) In humans, microbes that assist in digestion live in the large intestine. (Horses and humans are both postgastric fermenters.)

3. Compare the function of the stomach in the cow, horse, and human. Also, comment on the ability of each organism to digest cellulose in the stomach.

   The cow, as a ruminant, has multiple chambers in its stomach, two of which contain microbes capable of digesting cellulose. The other two chambers remove water and secrete enzymes to further break down the food as it moves into the small intestine. The stomach of horses and humans secretes enzymes to break down food, but cellulose is not broken down in the stomach of either animal.

4. The function and structure of the digestive tracts of the cow, horse, and human fit the diets of these animals. The grazers eat primarily leafy vegetation. Omnivores, however, consume more calories from plant storage structures (grains, tubers, and roots) than from leaves. Compare the relative sizes and functions of the digestive systems in grazers and omnivores.

   The grazers (cow and horse) have exceptionally long digestive systems adapted for a diet of plant materials. The highly concentrated pockets of microbes along the digestive tract facilitate the breakdown of cellulose. In humans, food digestion occurs in the stomach and small intestine, with some microbial digestion occurring in the large intestine. By the time "food" reaches the large intestine, little digestible material remains.

5. Once a horse swallows a bolus of food and it enters the stomach, strong muscles at the cardiac end of the stomach prevent the animal from regurgitating its food. How does this differ from the swallowing process in ruminants?

The ruminant swallows a bolus of food that may go to either the rumen or the reticulum. The cow periodically regurgitates the food and chews the cud, further breaking apart the plant structures to expose more cellulose for more microbial digestion. Only then does the well-digested food move into the small intestine for absorption. The horse does not produce cud because regurgitation is not part of its digestive process. Once the food enters the digestive tract, it passes through in one direction.

6. The digestion of what type of macromolecule begins in the organism's stomach (the abomasum in ruminants)?

Proteins are the macromolecules that undergo the most digestion in the stomach (or abomasum), although large carbohydrates may also undergo acid hydrolysis.

7. The small intestine functions similarly in all three organisms. Describe its function.

The small intestine is where further digestion of all classes of macromolecules occurs, facilitated by enzymes from the pancreas, liver, and other glands in the intestinal walls. Bile is added to the small intestine to facilitate fat digestion. Nutrients are absorbed from the small intestine wall into the bloodstream and the lymph.

8. The hindgut (structure of the digestive tract after the small intestine) in all three organisms contains a diverse population of fermenting microbes. These microbes release gases, as well as fatty acids and lactic acid as waste products of fermentation. Of the three organisms, the most hindgut fermentation occurs in horses.

   If a horse feeds on too much starchy grain, a lot of undigested carbohydrate will pass from the foregut into the hindgut. The same digestion problem happens when a horse feeds on spring grasses in the pasture. Grass plants produce many carbohydrate-rich leaves during the spring, but in the summer they produce more stem than leaf. Microbes that ferment the excess starch produce an increased level of lactic acid, which lowers the pH of the hindgut. Digestion in the hindgut stops and the horse often has to be treated for impaction. Why do you suppose excess starch halts digestion?

As discussed in the case Bean Brew, *many microbes cannot withstand a change in pH. When pH drops because of the fermentation of excess starch, many microbes that ferment cellulose to fatty acids are killed. Without the microbes, the cellulose-rich material in the hindgut is not digested and is not moved out of the horse's digestive tract, despite continuing peristalsis.*

9. The ecology of digestion relies on the presence of the right balance of microbial populations. For example, over a long period of time, antibiotic treatments can affect digestion in humans, and

there are similar effects in cows and horses. Describe the effect of antibiotics and the consequences to digestion.

On extended courses of antibiotics, most individuals develop diarrhea and loose stool. This is because normal microbial flora is wiped out and digestive processes in the small and large intestine do not function normally.

10. Cows, horses, and humans all consume foods containing cellulose. However, none of these organisms produces enzymes that can break down cellulose. Fermenting microbes in the stomach of cows convert cellulose to energy-rich fatty acids. Explain the fate of cellulose in horses and humans.

    Humans have neither the enzymes nor the appropriate microbes to digest cellulose and reap nutritional benefits. Cellulose in the human digestive tract is called "roughage" and is passed through the body and eliminated in the feces. Although humans do not gain nutrition from cellulose, it does give bulk to stool, which makes it easier to pass.

    Horses, as grazers, eat primarily cellulose-rich plants. They do have the appropriate microbes to obtain nutrients from cellulose. Digestion of cellulose occurs after it passes through the stomach and the small intestine. In the cecum and the large intestine, the microbes convert cellulose to fatty acids that are absorbed through the walls of the hindgut.

II. Feeding Horses

Wild horses are grazers that feed freely in grasslands. Their diet consists mainly of grasses and forbs (nongrass flowering plants). Domesticated horses are provided fewer choices. They are given access to either grass forage or hay that provides all or most of their required nutrients. To offset deficits in the quality and quantity of grass forage and hay, supplemental feed is provided. Often this feed contains additional vitamins and minerals and specialty feeds such as oats or corn.

1. Grass forage and hay consist largely of structural carbohydrates in the form of fiber, primarily cellulose. The fiber provides the raw material necessary for the growth and maintenance of microbial flora required for good horse health. We know that fiber is processed mainly in the hindgut. However, where does the processing of the fiber begin?

   Mechanical digestion begins in the mouth when teeth crop the fiber. (Horses do not secrete salivary amylase.)

2. When the yearling in the case showed signs of low weight gain, he was removed from the pasture. The owners increased his total amount of feed and provided a higher proportion of supplemental feed. The supplemental feed consisted of a mixture of lysine-rich field peas and cereal grains containing methionine and cystine. Why do you think the owners decided to incorporate more amino acids in the yearling's diet?

   Horses require protein for growth, muscle development, skin and hair development, and body tissue repair. By consuming more supplemental feed, the yearling will obtain more essential amino acids. These feed changes balance the relative amino acid proportions of the protein breakdown products from other feeds, to more closely fit the horse's requirements. The yearling's growth and, especially, its need to build lots of protein for muscles demand this kind of supplementation.

3. Weight status and activity levels can be used to estimate the amount of feed needed by individual horses (Figure 7.4). According to this chart, should you feed a horse with a normal weight of 1,150 pounds that engages in hard activity more total feed than a horse with a normal weight of 1,150 pounds that engages in light activity?

The total feed is the same.

Calculating Daily Feed for Horses

Weight 1,150 lb				
Activity	**Status**	**Total Feed (lb)**	**Grass Forage**	**Supplemental Feed**
Light	Normal	23.00	17.25	5.75
Moderate	Normal	23.00	13.80	9.20
Hard	Normal	23.00	11.50	11.50
Light	Underweight	28.75	21.56	7.19
Moderate	Underweight	28.75	17.25	11.50
Hard	Underweight	28.75	14.38	14.38

Figure 7.4 Spreadsheet for determining daily feed mixes for normal and underweight horses based on a weight of 1,150 pounds.

4. Compare the proportions of grass forage and supplemental feed in the total feed mix for the normal-weight horse with hard activity and the normal-weight horse with light activity.

The normal-weight, hardworking horse receives 50% of its feed as grass forage and 50% as supplemental feed. A normal-weight, light-working horse receives 75% of its feed as grass forage and 25% as supplemental feed.

5. If you have an underweight horse that is worked hard and a horse of normal weight that is worked hard, which should receive the most total feed? Is there a difference in the ratio of grass forage to supplemental feed?

The underweight horse receives more total feed. However, both horses receive half their feed as grass and half as supplemental feed.

6. Some organisms that infect grass prove harmful to horses. When the mare in the case was pregnant, the owners had the pasture with tall fescue grass tested. Fescue can contain an endophytic fungus that produces ergot alkaloids that are chemically similar to neurotransmitters (Browning, 2003). These alkaloids can interfere with the physiological control of labor and delivery as well as the survival of the foal. Should a pregnant mare be removed from a pasture infected with this fungus and fed solely supplemental feed?

The pregnant mare would need either grass forage in a different pasture or hay. Supplemental feed alone would not provide the long fiber needed.

7. In the case, the crowding of buffalo in a neighbor's pasture is criticized. Overcrowding limits available forage and substantially increases the potential for parasite infection. Parasites can be picked up when animals eat the larvae of flatworms and roundworms living in their pasture feed. How do the larvae of these animal parasites get into the grass?

Infected animals shed the parasites as they defecate. Animal wastes (dung) house the parasites until another animal eats a portion of these wastes on grass.

8. Easy-keeper horses are usually insulin-resistant. Because their bodies do not respond to normal insulin levels, they maintain abnormally high levels of insulin compared with horses that are not easy keepers. Easy keeper horses tend to convert excess carbohydrates to fat and require less food to maintain their weight. Easy keepers easily become overweight on supplemental feed. How might this genetic trait be beneficial to horses and to their owners?

This genetic trait may have adaptive value for horse populations that periodically suffer from drought and famine conditions. Certainly maintenance and feeding of all horses require skill and judgment, but easy keepers are less prone to suffer from underfeeding. Easy keepers are also cheaper to feed.

9. Owners of racehorses add oats to the supplemental feed to provide both extra protein for muscle repair and extra carbohydrates for the quick energy needed by these active horses. The excess starch in oats is processed in the large intestine. As you have learned, this may cause problems in horses. One proposed preventive treatment is to add a microbial amylase that functions at a wide range of pH to the supplemental feed. How could this help?

Amylase is an enzyme that catalyzes the breakdown of starches into sugars. The added enzyme ensures that more starches will be broken down in the small intestine. (The enzyme used in this circumstance is artificial and remains functional after passing through a horse's stomach.)

Suggested Answers for Additional Investigations

III. Reproduction in Mammals

A. Reproduction in *Equus.* After giving Leah the rest of the tour, Jim and Gina pointed out a pasture near their farm that contained a male zebra and a female donkey. Their healthy offspring, born earlier that year, was easily seen as it stood near the fence. Leah said, "Look at that weird little striped donkey. What is that?"

"We're guessing the donkey and zebra got together," Jim said.

"It's called a zonkey," Gina added.

"So does that mean a zebra is just a donkey with stripes?" Leah wondered aloud.

(See Figure 7.5 for images of these three animals.)

Horse, donkey, and zebra species all belong to the genus *Equus*. When two different species from *Equus* such as a horse and a donkey mate, they may produce hybrid offspring. (See the mule in Figure 24.4 in your text.)

(b) The zonkey and its dam—a donkey

(a) Male zebra who sired the zonkey

(c) The yearling zonkey

Figure 7.5 This yearling zonkey is an offspring of a male zebra and a female donkey.

1. Using the data in Table 7.1, determine the zonkey's parents. Explain.

Table 7.1 Diploid Chromosome Numbers in Various Equid Mammals.

Equid Mammal	Total Chromosome Number
African zebra	44
Mountain zebra	32
Donkey	62
Zonkey	53

The parents are the African zebra and the donkey. The gametes produced by the zebra have a haploid number of 22 and the gametes produced by the donkey have a haploid number of 31. The union of gametes produces 53 chromosomes in a zonkey embryo.

2. Although zebras and donkeys can produce offspring, do you think these two types of organisms should be considered to be the same species? Explain, using definitions of "species" and examples of prezygotic and postzygotic isolating mechanisms (see Chapter 24).

   No. The two should not be considered the same species. Prezygotic isolating barrier: There is little chance that a donkey and a zebra would mate under natural circumstances. The species would be more apt to choose members of their own species, based on physical and behavioral attributes. Postzygotic isolating barrier: Although the mating of a donkey and a zebra does result in healthy offspring, zonkeys most likely cannot breed successfully because of their odd number of chromosomes. According to the biological species concept organisms should be considered the same species only if they can mate and produce viable, fertile offspring.

3. Examine the photos in Figure 7.5 and list 3 traits of the zonkey that are different from its dam.

   Examples could include stripes, larger size even though it is a yearling, shorter ears, different facial markings, and wider skull.

B. Gestation in Mammals. Gestation is the period of time in which developing young are carried within the uterus. Table 7.2 shows the average gestation period for different placental mammals. *(Note: Whereas gestation time usually is calculated as the time from fertilization to birth, some smaller placental mammals such as squirrels and minks have delayed implantation. In this case, gestation refers only to the total time of active development.)*

1. Provide a hypothesis about the length of gestation with respect to the animals involved. For example, the larger the typical litter, the shorter the gestation period.

Table 7.2 Approximate Gestation Periods for Placental Mammals.

Mammal	Approximate Length of Gestation	
Mouse	19 days	
Rabbit	31 days	
Dog	61–63 days	
Cat	63–65 days	
Pig	112 days	
Goat, pygmy	145 days	
Goat	150 days	
Deer	201 days	
Human	266 days	
Cow	284 days	
Bison	285 days	
Horse	330–340 days	
Giraffe	457 days	
Elephant, Asian	645 days	

Students may propose many different hypotheses. Here is one possibility—As the size of the organism increases, so does the gestation period.

2. What single data column would you add to Table 7.2 to help you test your hypothesis?

Obtain the average sizes of these organisms (mass, length) as adults.

3. Choose six of the mammals in the table and look up the data for each. Enter your results in the blank column. (Don't forget to write in a column heading.)

Students should supply data on animal mass.

4. **a.** To test your hypothesis, construct a line graph with the data from the table. What will be on the *x*-axis of the graph? What will be on the *y*-axis of the graph?

Create a graph with the x-axis as mass (or whatever variable was selected) and y-axis as length of gestation.

b. Plot your graph in the space below.

The independent variable (selected by the student) on the x-axis and the dependent variable (in this case, length of gestation) on the y-axis will be appropriate. Look also for appropriate units, equivalent spacing, labels, and a title. This graph should be a line graph because the independent variable is continuously varying.

c. Interpret the graph. Are the results what you expected?

Students should discuss the shape of the line and what it tells about the relationship between the two variables. For example, as the size of the animal increases, the length of gestation increases, as shown by the line going up to the right. (Note: This would be a good place to introduce regression analysis if additional data for each type of animal are provided.)

IV. A Closer Look at Horse Evolution

In "Critical Reading," some of the evolutionary adaptations found in the digestive systems of grazing animals were considered. In this section, further adaptations found in modern horses and in fossils of equids (horselike organisms) will be examined.

1. To gain an overview of over 50 million years of horse evolution, examine Figure 25.25, the branched evolution of horses (cladogenesis). At one time, horse evolution was often depicted as a straight line—implying that an accumulation of changes gradually transformed one species into a species with different characteristics (anagenesis). (See Figure 7.6.) How does the shape of the more modern phylogenetic tree contradict the impression that one equid taxon died out as the next taxon emerged?

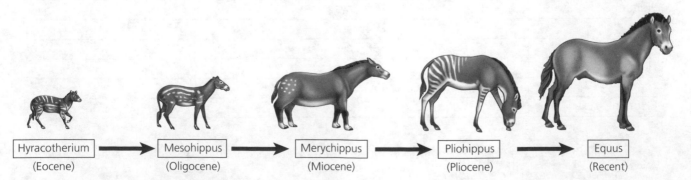

| Hyracotherium | Mesohippus | Merychippus | Pliohippus | Equus |
| (Eocene) | (Oligocene) | (Miocene) | (Pliocene) | (Recent) |

Figure 7.6 An example of how older diagrams depicted horse evolution as a straight line.

The tree shown in the text shows many branching points and many extinct taxa. It is not a single branch from Hyracotherium to Equus. The only living taxon of this tree is the genus Equus, which includes horses, donkeys, and zebras.

2. Go to "Wild Horses—An American Romance" at http://net.unl.edu/artsFeat/wildhorses/wh_origin/wh_origin2.html and explore the interactive phylogenetic tree of horses. Compare the tree to the time line of horse evaluation at http://net.unl.edu/artsFeat/wh_origin/wh_origin.html. What information does this interactive tree and time line provide as compared to Figure 25.25?

Answers will vary but students may suggest:

- *The time line gives specifics about each fossil.*
- *On time line, you can clearly see which taxa was present when.*
- *The bushlike representation of horse evolution is correlated to the periods. Its unlabeled lines suggest there may be more fossils, yet to find.*
- *The tree image suggests horses evolved over 55 million years.*

3. Summarize the changes in feeding habits, foot structure, and overall size of the animals depicted in Figure 25.25 on the one branch leading from *Hyracotherium* to *Equus*. (Note that the trends you see on this branch did not occur together or at a steady rate. They may have occurred in several branches of this evolutionary tree at different times. Evolution is not goal-oriented.)

Early ancestors of today's horses were browsers. Their teeth were adapted for eating woody shrubs and trees. In the early Miocene, the first groups adapted for grazing emerged. Modern equines are grazers, with teeth adapted for grinding tougher, grassy materials.

The foot structure evolved from four separate toes to three, then to only one that touched the ground with two smaller side toes higher than the ground. In more modern horses, the two side bones are fused together. Modern horses are of much greater size than Hyracotherium.

4. Examine Figure 7.7. Compare the teeth of the extinct and extant equid jaws.

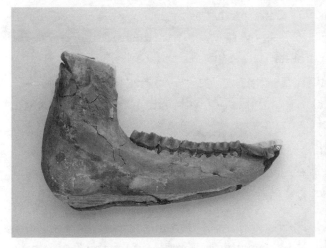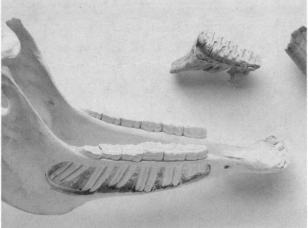

Figure 7.7 Jaws with teeth from equid of 18 million years ago (left), compared with jaws from a modern horse (right). Note that the modern jaw is much larger than the fossil jaw.
Source: Philip Dowell/Dorling Kindersley (left); Colin Keates/Dorling Kindersley, Courtesy of the Natural History Museum, London (right).

The teeth of the extinct equid are ridged and sharp-looking on the edges. Today's horse has much larger and flatter teeth, with lower ridges.

5. What kind of food did the extinct equid likely eat?

The extinct equid was probably a browser and ate woody plants. The sharp sides of its teeth would help in tipping tougher bark, and the inner smoother surfaces would then crush the plant material.

6. Although well adapted for running, modern horses are susceptible to a foot condition called laminitis, a deterioration of connective tissues within the hoof (Figure 7.8). Strong fibrous tissues called laminae occupy the space between the bone and hoof. The laminae support the terminal bone (3rd phalanx) and connect it to the hoof wall. In horses suffering from laminitis, these connective tissues become swollen and then detached, allowing the bones to twist, penetrate the hoof, or sink within the hoof. If not properly treated, the animal will become lame. In some cases the lameness can be remedied, but sometimes the lameness is so debilitating that the animal needs to be euthanized.

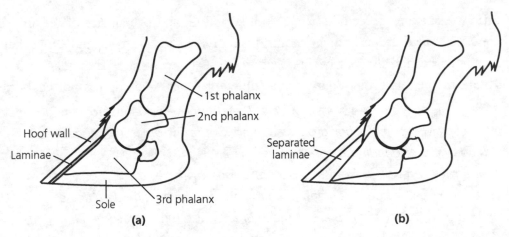

Figure 7.8 Laminitis. (a) Normal foot anatomy. (b) Foot of horse with laminitis. Note the shifting bone structure.

Although the cause of laminitis is not known, many predisposing factors have been correlated with the onset of laminitis. One of these factors is overfeeding with lush spring grasses or other sources of high carbohydrates. One hypothesis is that the excess carbohydrates lead to toxins in the blood that irritate the sensitive laminae.

What are some differences between the normal foot and the foot with laminitis? Consider where the weight of the horse is placed.

In b, the 3rd phalanx has rotated so that it is pointing down. The weight of the horse is on the very tip of this bone instead of spread out across its flat surface. (In severe cases of laminitis, the third phalanx may rotate until it actually breaks through the sole.)

7. Raising horses is at best an artificial system in which the horse's normal movement, choice of feed, population size, and breeding are restricted. What evolutionary implications might this have for future domesticated horse populations?

Horses that survive under these artificial selection pressures may exhibit a reduction in genetic variability at the population level due to artificial selection for certain traits. (Other traits, however, may actually exhibit more variation because they are free from artificial selection.) These effects may involve a loss of fitness under free-range conditions. For example, horse populations bred for size or racing ability under high-maintenance diets may be less efficient grazers. Many breeders prefer "easy keepers"— horses that are usually insulin-resistant and store excess glucose as fat. When these horses have well-maintained diets, this is not a problem. However, changes in diet can lead to laminitis and other disorders.

V. Open-Ended Investigations

Go to the Case Book website at http://bioquest.org/icbl/casebook to access a live copy of the Excel spreedsheet on feeding horses. Investigate scenarios provided there or make up your own.

References

Browning, R., Jr. 2003. "Tall Fescue Endophyte Toxicosis in Beef Cattle: Clinical Mode of Action and Potential Mitigation Through Cattle Genetics," 2003. http://www.bifconference.com/bif2003/BIFsymposium_pdfs/Browning.pdf

Ensminger, M. E., and C. G. Olentine. 1978. *Feeds and Nutrition*. Clovis, CA: The Ensminger Publishing Company, 1978.

Fossil Horse Cybermuseum. http://www.flmnh.ufl.edu/natsci/vertpaleo/fhc/firstCM.htm (accessed October 11, 2007).

Hunt, K. 1995. "Horse Evolution." http://www.talkorigins.org/faqs/horses/horse_evol.html

Chapter 8:

Back to the Bay

INSTRUCTOR'S GUIDE

As with all the cases in this book, please read the preface if you have not already done so. In the preface you will find suggestions about using Investigative Case–Based Learning (ICBL) for different instructional purposes such as starting a new lecture topic, assessing what students already know, setting a context for lab activities, and so on. The preface also describes ways to use cases in a variety of classroom settings and suggests multiple ways to assess learning with cases.

Back to the Bay accompanies Unit Eight: Ecology in Campbell and Reece's *Biology*, 8th edition. The case emphasizes material covered in Chapter 51: Behavioral Ecology and provides cues that will lead students to look at sections in other chapters of Unit Eight. There are four strands in the case:

- Behavior
- Alternatives for control of gulls
- Population dynamics
- Link between the human population and the health of the Chesapeake Bay

Students should complete the Case Analysis immediately following the reading of the case. We strongly suggest that students work in groups to complete the Case Analysis. Actively listening to and challenging the ideas of others can help learners become aware of their own misconceptions, yet value their own and others' prior knowledge.

Seven investigations accompany *Back to the Bay*. Five are "core" investigations relating directly to the facts of the case, one is an additional investigation that extends beyond the case and into other chapters in the ecology unit, and one is an open-ended investigation of gull population growth and control. Table IG8.1 describes what students will gain from each investigation.

Table IG8.1 Back to the Bay Case Overview.

Investigation	Learning Goals	Inquiry Skills Used
Core Investigations		
I. Critical Reading	Students use Chapter 51 for information to support their speculations on types of behaviors described in the case.	• developing ideas based on evidence and resources
II. Design an Experiment	Students design an experiment that would test whether or not response to distress calls by gulls is learned.	• using information on designing experiments from text • writing hypotheses • designing controlled experiments • defining variables • predicting results if the hypothesis is supported
III. Investigation of Gull Call Advertisement	Students examine an advertisement for a hypothetical product and are asked to think critically and scientifically about biological claims in the advertisement.	• applying science to advertising claims
IV. Investigations of Population Growth and Control	Students will interpret data on four different gull populations and speculate on reasons for the differences in population growth. A model based on clutch size, survivorship, and other factors allows students to test their ideas about effective control methods.	• interpreting data tables • recognizing limited data • drawing conclusions • using models • evaluating control methods using data
V. Explore the Environmental Conditions of the Chesapeake Bay	This activity extends to several other chapters in the Ecology unit of Campbell. Students visit interactive, data-rich sites about the Chesapeake. They select and then analyze data regarding the biodiversity of the Bay.	• working with large data sets • extracting and interpreting information
Additional Investigations		
VI. Ethics Paper on Gull and Human Interactions	Students are given a list of interactions between gulls and humans to research. The suggested student product is a 1-or 2-page paper. A second option is for the more business-minded. Both options use links located on the Case Book website.	• summarizing information • writing concisely about biological situations • considering the ethical dimensions of human-gull interactions
VII. Open-Ended Investigations	Gull population growth and control may be explored with Excel models.	• manipulating variables • using Excel-based models • reasoning quantitatively

Table IG8.2 contains several resources related to *Biology*, 8th edition, that will help your students further their understanding of this case. Note that chapter readings and activities are listed in order of importance in regard to the case.

Table IG8.2 Campbell-Related Resources.

Resource	Chapter/Activity	Topics Covered/Activity Titles
Critical Reading from *Biology*, 8th edition	Chapter 51: Animal Behavior	Entire chapter
Related Readings	Chapter 52: An Introduction to Ecology and the Biosphere	Dispersal and distribution (Concept 52.2); aquatic biomes (Concept 52.4)
	Chapter 53: Population Ecology	Population limiting factors (Concept 53.5); human population growth (Concept 53.6)
	Chapter 54: Community Ecology	Food webs (Concept 54.2); human disturbance (Concept 54.3); theories of community (Concept 54.5)
	Chapter 55: Ecosystems	Nutrient cycling (Concept 55.4); human impact on ecosystems (Concept 55.5)
	Chapter 56: Conservation Biology and Restoration Ecology	Biodiversity and human welfare, human threats to biodiversity (Concept 56.1); extinction vortex (Concept 56.2)
Campbell website/ CD-ROM	Chapter 51 **Investigation**	How Can Pillbug Responses to Environments Be Tested? (This will help students with designing controlled experiments.)
	Lab Bench	Animal Behavior (Students observe drawings of the *Drosophila* mating dance and then design an experiment to investigate some aspect of mating behavior.)
	Video	Albatross Courtship Ritual (Students can practice observation skills while watching this video.)
	Chapter 52 **Activity**	Science, Technology, and Society: DDT
Morgan/Carter *Investigating Biology*, 5e	Lab Topic 1	Scientific Investigation
	Lab Topic 26	Animal Behavior (Students observe different behaviors in lab animals, such as taxis in brine shrimp, kinesis in pillbugs, and agnostic display in male Siamese fighting fish.)

Case Narrative

Students were asked to underline terms or phrases in the introductory narrative that they think are important to understanding the case. Suggested terms and phrases that students might have chosen are in bold type.

Descended from oystermen and crabbers, Liam and Solana looked forward to their family reunion at **Maryland's Chesapeake Bay.** Although this section of the Bay **no longer supports commercial shell fishing** there was plenty to see.

While **waiting in line** to purchase tickets for a boat tour of the bay, Liam and Solana heard a **series of screeches.** They scanned the docks for the source of the mayhem. **A large gull that had settled on a covered boat hurriedly flew away midway through the screeches.** After several more seconds, **the noise stopped.**

"What *was* that?" Solana asked. "It sounds like birds are being attacked, but I don't see anything." Liam just shrugged and pointed out **a mallard still floating a few feet from the dock and a tern still sitting on the nearby pilings despite the noise.** "Can't they hear? They'd have to be deaf to ignore that," Solana said.

The woman working at the nearby snack stand looked up and offered an explanation. "Well, **it's a tape the marina owner is using to scare the gulls away. Seems like there's more every year. Gull droppings cause holes in the boat covers if they aren't cleaned quickly.** We've tried everything to keep the gulls away.

"The marina owner found an ad for this tape on the Internet. He says there are **six different gull distress calls,** which are all supposed to sound just like the real thing. The tape **plays every couple of hours during the day.** It **worked great last summer, but lately some of the gulls seem to ignore it.**

"The owner of the next marina over even keeps a **few dead gulls out on the dock. He claims it keeps the tapes working, but I . . ."**

"Look at that," Liam interrupted. "Someone used duct tape to block the speaker at this end of the dock."

Squinting her eyes to get a better look at the speaker, the woman nodded. "I bet the guy in the 22-foot Sea Ray did it," she offered. "He claims that it's **the new landfill causing the gull problem in the first place,** and we should get rid of that rather than disturb his peace."

"Well, at least the tape still seems to be working on him," observed Liam, laughing.

Suggested Answers for Case Analysis

1. **Recognize potential issues and major topics in the case.** What is this case about? Underline and list terms or phrases that seem to be important to understanding this case. Then list **3–4** biology-related topics or issues in the case.

   Biology-related topics or issues: rapidly increasing gull populations, human interactions with natural ecosystems, demise of shell fishing on the Bay, gull control methods, use of bird calls as a deterrent, species specificity of calls

2. **What specific questions do you have about these topics?** By yourself, or better yet, in a group, make a list of the things you already know about this case in the "What Do I Know?" column. List questions you would like to learn more about in the "What Do I Need to Know?" column.

   There are many possible answers, depending on the experiences of your students. Some likely responses follow.

What Do I Know?	What Do I Need to Know?
• The Chesapeake is in Maryland (perhaps some students will have visited the area and can add more here). • Many people live near the Chesapeake. • Loss of shell fishing. • Gulls are a problem. • Landfills are gull-feeding areas. • Gulls can live inland—a real problem on large lakes, inland dumps. • Case suggests there are many gull control methods. • Birds sometimes get caught in airplane engines and cause crashes.	• What does the gull distress call sound like? • How do gull distress calls work under natural conditions? As a gull control? • Why are some birds not responding to the call? • Why is shell fishing no longer possible in the Bay? • How does a landfill relate to larger gull populations? • What are other control methods besides the tapes? • What do oystermen and crabbers do?

3. Put a check mark by **1–3** questions or issues from the "What Do I Need to Know?" list that you think are most important to explore.

   You should expect a range of responses. Most students will identify ecological questions since they are in a biology class and beginning the ecology unit.

4. **What kinds of references or resources would help you answer or explore these questions?** Identify two different resources and explain what information each resource is likely to give that will help you answer the question(s). Choose specific resources.

   Accept any reasonable resource (e.g., text, other book, Internet sites, maps, data tables, and so on) that could be related to the case. The answer "the Web" is too vague. Students should explain the type of site they are looking for or search terms they might use.

Suggested Answers for Core Investigations

I. Critical Reading

Read Chapter 51: Animal Behavior, which discusses several kinds of animal behavior. Listed below are descriptions of various responses displayed by birds in the case. Answer the questions that follow each response. Provide examples from Chapter 51 to support your answers. As you complete this exercise, note that, behaviorally speaking, distress calls are similar to the alarm calls you read about in the text.

1. Only one species of gull leaves the area when the tape plays.

   a. Explain the gulls' response.

   The gulls hear this noise and they leave the area. We know already that other birds do not respond, so this series of sounds is likely one that gulls recognize as a specific noise with specific meaning.

   b. Do you think this response is primarily learned or primarily genetic? Explain.

   We can't tell if this response is primarily learned or genetic without more information on how infant, juvenile, and adult gulls react to the same call. However, the text suggests that alarm calls are socially learned in other species.

   c. Could the call be categorized as a signal? Explain.

   It is definitely a signal, "a behavior that causes a change in another animal's behavior."

2. A year later, the same species of gull remains when the tape plays.

   a. What might account for the change in the gulls' response?

   The gulls ignore the call because there has been no real cause for alarm for a year, despite repeated calls.

   b. Do you think this response is primarily learned or primarily genetic? Explain.

   This is likely learned because the conditions have not changed, just the gulls' response to the stimulus. This behavior suggests that the response is not a fixed action pattern.

   c. Speculate on what kinds of behavior this response might be.

   This might be habituation.

   d. How does this behavior exemplify the "cry wolf" effect? Explain this in terms of a cost-benefit analysis.

   In this case, the gulls stop responding to a distress call when no evidence of distress accompanies the call—the "cry wolf" effect. (This could also be associative learning.) There is neither reward for leaving the site causing distress nor penalty for staying. By ignoring a useless warning, the gulls are using more of the environment. A cost-benefit analysis might suggest that learning to detect the cry wolf effect may benefit the organism through energy saving.

3. The same species of gull resumes its response to the tape when dead gulls are displayed in the immediate area of the sound.

    a. What might account for the change in the gulls' response?

       The gulls notice dead gulls at the same time they hear the distress call. They now respond by leaving the area where it appears gulls are dying.

    b. Do you think this response is primarily learned or primarily genetic? Explain.

       This would suggest that gulls are capable of learning, of processing information and distinguishing between a "false alarm" and the real thing.

    c. How does this behavior reflect associative learning? Is it negative or positive reinforcement?

       This may be a way to overcome the cry wolf effect, as the birds observe that real danger exists, which could result in death. The addition of the second stimulus and the gulls' response to it could be an example of associate learning, particularly negative reinforcement.

    d. Can this behavior be interpreted as altruistic? Explain.

       This situation may be an example of altruistic behavior. One gull gives the alarm signal and the others "save themselves." If the one sounding the alarm is killed or significantly endangered in giving the call, then this would be altruism.

4. Birds other than this gull species ignore the taped distress calls.

    a. What might account for the observed behavior in the other birds?

       Even if other birds can hear the gull distress calls, they are not signals that they respond to by either learned or genetic responses.

    b. Researchers switched young of one species of bird with those of another. The young birds responded to the signals of the new species. Do you think this response is primarily learned or primarily genetic? Explain.

       Learned. It varies by age.

    c. What evidence do you have from the case to support the idea that calls are species specific?

       The lack of response by the mallard and the tern suggests that the calls on the tape are species-specific, and that birds can discriminate among sounds in the environment to respond to only those that have meaning for them.

5. You observe that some gulls continue to respond to taped distress calls when *no* danger is present. Do you think that these gulls are more or less fit than those that stop responding to such calls? Explain.

    The gulls that continue to respond are less fit. The gulls that ignore the false calls (become habituated) would increase their fitness. They no longer expend the energy to fly away, perhaps from a beneficial food source. The birds that continue to respond are decreasing their fitness because the danger is not real and they are expending energy for no reason.

II. Design an Experiment

Design an experiment to examine the following question. Is the response to distress calls (moving away from the area) learned in herring gulls?

Materials: You will have access to newly hatched, juvenile, and adult herring gulls. You also will have a tape of herring gull distress calls.

The following additional resources may help you with this activity:

Web/CD Chapter 51 Investigation, How Can Pillbug Responses to the Environment Be Tested? *and Lab Topic 1 of* Investigating Biology *by Morgan and Carter.*

1. Restate the question being studied as a testable hypothesis.

   The age of the bird affects how it will respond to a distress call. If the response is learned, younger birds will have fewer appropriate responses than older birds.

2. Describe the experiment.

   a. What will the treatment(s) be? Which animals will receive each treatment?

   Note: There are many possible experimental designs with these materials. Look for well-controlled experiments that allow for meaningful measurements of responses to distress calls. Most designs will segregate birds into groups that have an opportunity to learn from adults and groups without this opportunity.

   b. What will you measure as the response to the treatment?

   The movements of the birds when the distress calls are played. Expected response is a movement away from the source of the call.

3. List 3 variables that you will control.

   Age of the birds when subjected to the tapes, where the tapes are played, the loudness and duration of the taped distress calls, use of the same tape or a different tape, use of a controlled environment with lights approximating daylight.

4. Describe the experimental results that would support your hypothesis.

   Younger birds should show statistically significant differences in response to distress calls from older birds.

III. Biology in Advertising

Examine the advertisement for a gull distress call recording in Figure 8.2 and answer the following questions.

Gull Gone *Marina Mate*

Searching for a way to safely keep gulls away from boats, docks, and the shore? Order Gull Gone today and reduce the damage caused by overpopulation of these pests.

- Distress calls from seven gull species including Herring Gull, Laughing Gull, and Ring-Billed Gull.
- Select only the distress calls you need.
- Program the calls to a specific schedule or just set on random play.
- Speaker volume adjustable. Effective up to 200 feet away.
- Operates on photocell only; operational during active period for gulls.
- Includes booklet on maximizing effective bird pest control.
- Field tested—effective in driving gulls away when operated as recommended.
- Audible Range: 100–110 dB (decibel).
- One-year unconditional money-back guarantee.
- UL and CE listed. Made in the USA.
- Shipping wt.: 7 lb

Contact us at: gullgone@marina.com for more information.

To order call: (555) 555-0099

Figure 8.2 Advertisement for *"Gull Gone."*

1. What are three biological claims in this advertisement?

   Different species of gulls have different distress calls.

   Gulls only respond to their own species' distress calls.

   Gulls sleep at night (dark) and are active during the day (light).

   Gulls respond to taped calls.

   Gull calls are in the 100–110 decibel range.

   The advertisement implies that there are ways to maximize gull responses.

2. Choose one of the claims and briefly describe an experiment that would test its validity.

There are many possible answers. A good answer will describe at least one experimental and one control condition, as well as what is being measured. Here are some examples:

- *In order to find out if gull responses to distress calls are species-specific, use a distress call from a different species and observe gull reaction.*

- *In order to determine if gulls are active other than in daylight hours, observe them during both night and day.*

- *In order to see if gulls habituate to distress calls that occur at regular intervals, run a long-term experiment providing distress calls at set times at one site and at random times at another. Observe gull behavior.*

3. Is there any behavioral significance to the product's feature that allows for playing distress calls in random sequence?

The gulls do not have the opportunity to associate intermittent calls with specific times of the day. This reduces early habituation to the tape of distress calls.

IV. Investigations of Population Growth and Control

A. Gull Population Growth *(Refer to Chapter 53 in your text for help with this exercise.)*

1. Review the data in Table 8.1.

Table 8.1 Increase in Number of Gull Mating Pairs in Selected Locations.

Locations	Initial Observation Mating Pairs/Year	Final Observation Mating Pairs/Year	Gull Species
Kennedy Airport, New York, United States	15 pairs/1970	7,600 pairs/1990	Laughing Gull
Leslie Spit, Toronto, Canada	20 pairs/1973	80,000 pairs/1982	Ring-Billed Gull
Five Islands, Wollongong, New South Wales, Australia	3 pairs (est.)/1949	51,500 pairs/1978	Silver Gull
Mud Islands, Port Phillips Bay, Victoria, Australia	5 pairs/1959	70,000 pairs/1988	Silver Gull

a. Are the four gull populations all increasing in size at the same rate? Explain.

No, some are increasing faster than others. For example, ring-billed gulls in Toronto increased by 4,000 times in 9 years. Laughing gulls only increased about 500 times in 20 years.

b. Which rates are the most similar?

In the populations of silver gulls and of ring-billed gulls.

c. While doing further research on gull populations, you discover that in 1985 there were 15,000 pairs of laughing gulls living in the vicinity of John F. Kennedy International Airport in New York City. How does this knowledge change your answers to 1a and 1b?

The estimates of population rates will be higher for the New York site, although still lower than all the others.

2. Consider reasons why differences in these gull populations occur. List three ways that the environment in which the birds live could affect their rates of reproduction.

Gulls may have different clutch sizes (eggs per nest).

Incubation time for eggs.

Nestlings may require more food.

Young birds may remain in the nest for longer periods.

Male-to-female ratios in the populations.

Onset of breeding maturity in the juveniles.

Anti-predator behavior.

3. Population growth is greatly influenced by environmental factors. The activities of a human population impact nearby gull populations. For example, the potential for collisions between aircraft and gulls ensures that officials at John F. Kennedy International Airport implement gull population control measures. List at least three other examples of human-gull interactions. For each example, explain whether the gull population benefits.

Landfills—Gull population grows until control measures occur, then population decreases.

Commercial fishing sites—Attract gulls to processing areas. Gulls benefit.

Recreational beaches—Gulls are attracted to food and garbage.

Oil spills—Gulls are attracted to fish kills and are contaminated as well.

Feed lots—Gulls are attracted to and benefit from increased food.

B. Control of Bird Populations: The Chicken or the Egg? If the ultimate goal at an airport location is to reduce gull population size to ensure human safety, should gull nests and eggs or adult gulls be removed? In this exercise, you will use a model to compare the effectiveness of these two methods.

1. Fill in the worksheet in Figure 8.3 to estimate the relative effectiveness of these two different population control methods.

The Chicken or the Egg Worksheet		Method: No Control	Remove Adult Birds*	Remove Nests and Eggs
Find the differences in population growth resulting from two gull control methods.				
Assumptions				
Basic Population	Enter			
Adults = (2) (#nesting pairs) =	20	Nesting Pairs = 10	Nesting Pairs = 10	Nesting Pairs = 10
Total # eggs = (#eggs per nest) (#nesting pairs) =	30	Eggs per Nest = 3	Eggs per Nest = 3	Eggs per Nest = 3
Potential Population =	50	Survival of Adults = 90%	Survival of Adults =50%	Survival of Adults =90%
		Survival of Young Birds = 50%	Survival of Young Birds = 50%	Survival of Young Birds = 10%
Enter the values from the information above and perform the calculations.		No Control	Remove Adult Birds	Remove Nests and Eggs
Surviving Adults = (% survival) (#nesting pairs)(2)		(.90)(10)(2) = 18		
Surviving Chicks =(% survival)(#eggs per nest)(#nesting pairs)		(.50)(3)(10) = 15		
Surviving Population = Surviving Adults + Surviving Chicks		18 + 15 = 33		

*Note that the percentage of surviving young birds does not change when adult birds are removed because the adults are removed before they reproduce.

Figure 8.3 The Chicken or the Egg Worksheet. Use the provided equations to calculate surviving gull populations after implementing two types of gull control methods. This spreadsheet also is provided on the Case Book website as a functioning model. (Weisstein, 2004a)

Remove adult birds: 10 surviving adults, 15 surviving chicks, 25 in surviving population.

Remove nests and eggs: 18 surviving adults, 3 surviving chicks, 21 in surviving population.

2. Which of these gull control methods is more effective?

Nest and egg removal.

3. Which of these two control methods would you advocate? Explain your choice.

Expect this answer to be subjective. Students may choose on the basis of what the most effective method or preferential criterion is, such as a method that does not harm the birds. If the gull nests are in difficult-to-reach places such as vertical cliffs, it might be physically easier to remove adult birds.

V. Explore the Environmental Conditions of the Chesapeake Bay

Liam and Solana spent 4 hours on their boat tour of the Chesapeake Bay, learning about its history, ecology, and geology. In this investigation, you will take a brief "armchair tour" of the Chesapeake Bay by exploring some of the environmental factors that affect its biological diversity. Go to the Case Book website for resources on Chesapeake Bay and further directions for the following activities.

A. **Stressors on the Bay.** Examine the animation. List three important stressors on the Chesapeake (see the Stressors on the Bay link on the Case Book website).

Emissions, turbidity, high nutrient load, over-harvesting, toxicants introduced

B. **Cutter Marina.** Examine the information about Cutter Marina, including the data charts and interpretation of each of the water quality variables measured. Describe and provide the values for three variables that indicate a healthy bay.

Students may have described three of the following variables:

- *Dissolved oxygen above 5 mg/L.*

- *Appropriate salinities (drought can raise salinity to levels that the organisms cannot withstand). Ocean is 32 ppt (parts per thousand).*

- *pH 7 is neutral; range of 5.5–8.5 is usually tolerated by aquatic organisms. Lower pH may be found in marshes or caused by acid rain; higher pH may be caused by algal blooms.*

- *Turbidity: Light needs to penetrate the water for plant life to survive.*

- *Temperature: Most organisms are adapted to fluctuating temperatures, which occur on a daily and seasonal basis. Some factors, such as severe drought, could lead to extreme temperature changes. Those organisms with the ability to migrate to another area may do so.*

C. **Eyes on the Bay.** The water quality of the Chesapeake is sampled daily at more than 100 sampling stations. All of these data are reported and compiled online at "Eyes on the Bay" (Figure 8.4) whose link is listed on the Case Book website.

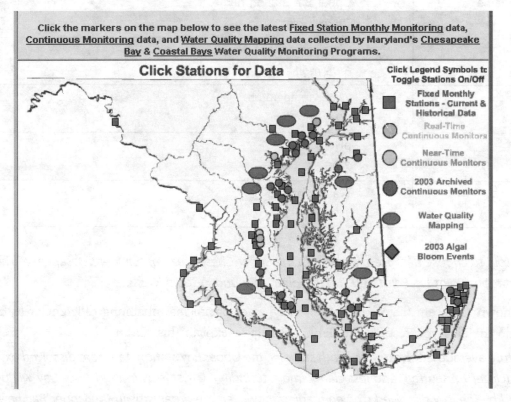

Figure 8.4 Eyes on the Bay.

1. At the Eyes on the Bay website, examine differences in salinity across the Chesapeake Bay by first switching to "full-screen map" and then running your cursor over the red square icons and reading the salinity data that appear on the left side of the screen.

　a. Describe what happens to salinity as you move from open ocean (the right and lower edges of the map) to the top of the Chesapeake Bay.

　　The salinity decreases as you move from the open ocean (18 ppt) to the mouth of the Bay (5–18 ppt). By the time you reach the head of the Bay, the salinity decreases to 0.5–5 ppt.

　b. Describe what happens to salinity as you move from the center of the Chesapeake Bay and up the Potomac River, which starts near the bottom center of the map.

　　At the mouth of the Bay, salinity is 5–18 ppt. Once you reach the mouth of the river, it falls to 0.5–5 ppt. Within the river, salinity levels are 0—considered fresh, but tidally influenced.

2. Choose data from two stations, one from the upper Chesapeake Bay and one from the lower Chesapeake Bay near the ocean. Click on the icon to open the station's site. Look at the following variables during August: dissolved oxygen, water temperature, pH, and water clarity. Enter the data for each station in Table 8.2.

Table IG8.3 Student Answers to Table 8.2

Year: _____ *e.g., 2002* _____
Month: August

Lower Bay station name: *Point No Point*	Upper Bay station name: *Turkey Point*
Dissolved oxygen *1.30 mg/L*	Dissolved oxygen *6.05 mg/L*
Water temperature *80.96°C*	Water temperature *80.96°C*
pH *8.0*	pH *7.06*
Water clarity *1.75 m*	Water clarity *1.05 m*

Students were told to choose data from stations in the upper Chesapeake and lower Chesapeake. The values for the stations Point No Point and Turkey Point are found in Table IG8.3.

3. Studies have shown there are major differences in types of organisms inhabiting different areas of the Bay. How do the data you recorded in Table 8.2 help to explain this finding?

While temperature average is the same for both stations, the Upper Bay station has more dissolved oxygen, lower pH (closer to neutral), and less clarity (more turbidity). Organisms in the Lower Bay will be severely stressed by the low dissolved oxygen reading; however, the organisms in the Upper Bay have access to plenty of oxygen. The higher turbidity in the Lower Bay will have a negative effect on sea grasses and other photosynthetic organisms. Overall, organisms must be well suited to the environmental conditions. Those withstanding higher turbidity and requiring more dissolved oxygen are better suited to the Upper Bay. Those organisms that need more light and can survive in a more basic environment with less dissolved oxygen are better suited to the Lower Bay.

D. Chesapeake Bay Remote Sensing Program. Go to the Case Book website to access the link to the "Chesapeake Bay Remote Sensing Program" website (Figure 8.5). Use this website to examine productivity in the Chesapeake as measured by chlorophyll production.

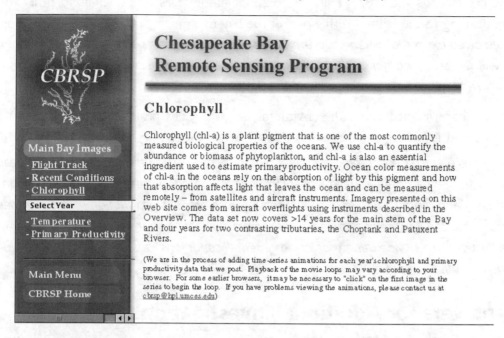

Figure 8.5 CBRSP ascertains chlorophyll concentrations to estimate primary productivity and to gauge the overall productivity of the Chesapeake Bay ecosystem.

1. Choose a year from 1998 to 2002 and run the animation of chlorophyll for the whole year. (*Note:* If you click on the animation while it is running, it will pause on the map shown. Double-clicking will resume the animation.) Briefly describe the changes in chlorophyll content in April, July, and October.

High levels of chlorophyll were present in April, mainly in the middle region of the Bay, with most recordings in the 12–25 mg/m³ range. In July, most of the Bay had higher chlorophyll readings, with the lower end of the range at the mouth of the Bay. Readings were primarily in the 16–30 mg/m³ range. By October the entire Bay ranged from 4–10 mg/m³, with most readings in the 6–8 mg/m³ range.

2. For the years 1998–2002, track chlorophyll data for the last reading in July. Focus on the grid square bounded by 37–37.5 (representing latitude) on the left and by 76.5–76 (representing longitude) on the bottom. Give a range and an average for each date in Table 8.3.

Table IG8.7 Student Answers to Table 8.3.

Date	Range/Average
July 1998	*Low of 6, high of 25, most 8–12 mg/m³*
July 1999	*Low of 2, high of 8, most 4–8 mg/m³*
July 2000	*Low of 6, high of 10, most 6–8 mg/m³*
July 2001	*Low of 2, high of 10, most 6–10 mg/m³*
July 2002	*Low of 2, high of 16, most 6–12 mg/m³*

3. Compare the data you tracked for 1998 and 1999. What might account for the differences you see in the chlorophyll increase for these 2 years?

   Variable answer: Could be temperature, rainfall, or effluents that promote algal growth.

4. The area of the Chesapeake Bay where Liam and Solana's family has lived is near the Lower Chester River, south of Eastern Neck Island (38.99 latitude, 76.22 longitude). Describe one variable that you think may be contributing to the failure of this part of the Bay to support commercial shell fishing. *Shellfish require dissolved oxygen of >5 mg/L. If the oyster beds no longer receive that much oxygen, then the oysters will die out. Another possible reason might be overharvesting of the oysters, thus removing them before they have time to repopulate the oyster beds.*

5. Summarize what you have learned about the environment of the Chesapeake Bay, comparing and contrasting the upper and lower regions of the Bay and the rivers that empty into the Bay.

   The Chesapeake Bay has many different regions, where biological processes differ throughout the year. The lower regions of the Bay are saltier, have less chlorophyll, and are less turbid. The upper regions of the Bay are less salty and more turbid, and have much more chlorophyll production in the summer. The rivers that empty into the Bay are salty for some of their distance, although less salty than the Bay, and are affected by tides. This wide variety of environmental conditions can account for the wide variety of organisms that live in the Bay.

Suggested Answers for Additional Investigations

VI. Ethics Paper on Gull and Human Interactions
(Students were told to choose A or B.)

Go to the Case Book website for links to information about many of these topics.

A. Choose one of the following situations in which humans and gulls interact.
   - Landfills
   - Airports
   - Offshore oil rigs
   - Roof-roosting gulls in Melbourne, Australia
   - Municipal reservoirs
   - Maintaining biodiversity in wildlife refuges
   - Maintaining biodiversity and gull effects
   - Protecting birds from oil spills using sound

   Research the situation examining control methods used and outcomes. Consider the impact of the large gull populations on the environment, other species, and humans. Then consider the impact of the control measures. Discuss the ethical issues involved in the decision to control a species and in the various control measures that were used.

A list of situations in which humans and gulls interact is included in the student investigation. Research resources are included on the Case Book website. In their papers, students should:

- *consider the impact of the large gull populations on the environment, other species, and humans.*

- *consider the impact of the control measures.*

- *discuss the ethical issues involved in the decision to control a species and in the various control measures that were used.*

B. Choose three of the following methods of gull control. Evaluate each for its effectiveness in controlling gulls, its expense, and the ethics of both using and selling these methods. Describe your findings in a 1- to 2-page paper.

- Model aircraft (Melbourne area)
- Owl effigies (Louisiana Land and Exploration)
- Rubber snakes (Tides Stadium, 1997)
- Avipoint installations to prevent roosting
- Raptors as gull predators
- Deterrent spray
- High-pressure water blaster (Melbourne area zoo)
- Monofilament lines (Melbourne area hotel)

Students were told to evaluate three methods of gull control for effectiveness, expense, and ethics of use. Students should turn in a 1- to 2-page paper. (See the student investigation for the list of gull control methods.)

VII. Open-Ended Investigations

You may explore gull population and control using either the "logistic growth" or "control and cost" Excel models (Weisstein, 2004b and 2004c) at http://bioquest.org/icbl/casebook/gullcontrol.

References

Chlorophyll animation. http://www.cbrsp.org/cbrsp_toc_mb_chl_page.htm. Accessed October 11, 2007.

Eyes on the Bay. http://mddnr.chesapeakebay.net/eyesonthebay/index.cfm. Accessed October 11, 2007.

Weisstein, Anthony. 2004a. Chicken or the Egg: Excel worksheet. All of these models are at http://bioquest.org/icbl/casebook/gullcontrol

Weisstein, Anthony. 2004b. Controlling cost: Excel worksheet.

Weisstein, Anthony. 2004c. Logistic growth: Excel worksheet.

Chapter 9:

Pandemic Flu (Past and Possible)

INSTRUCTOR'S GUIDE

As with all the cases in this book, please read the preface if you have not already done so. In the preface you will find suggestions about using Investigative Case–Based Learning (ICBL) in different instructional situations such as starting a new lecture topic, assessing what students already know, setting a context for lab activities, and so on. The preface also describes ways to use cases in a variety of classroom settings and suggests multiple ways to assess learning with cases.

Pandemic Flu (Past and Possible) emphasizes materials found in Chapter 19: Viruses and Chapter 43: The Immune System in Campbell and Reece's *Biology*, 8th edition. Pandemic Flu Past focuses on the 1918 influenza pandemic and uses an oral history. Pandemic Flu (Possible) uses current maps to introduce students to the H5N1 avian influenza A strain currently in the headlines. There are four strands in this chapter:

- Structure and function of the H5N1 variant
- The immune system
- Epidemiology of Avian Flu
- Mitigation, prevention, and treatment

The students should complete the Case Analysis immediately following the reading of the case. We strongly suggest that students work in groups to complete the Case Analysis. Actively listening to and challenging the ideas of others can help learners become aware of their own misconceptions, yet value their own and others' prior knowledge.

Seven investigations accompany *Pandemic Flu (Past and Possible)*. Five are "core" investigations relating directly to the facts of the case, and two are additional investigations that extend the case to other applications. Table IG9.1 describes what students will gain from each investigation. See the Case Book website for additional investigations with the SIR model, extended data sets from the 1918 influenza, and resources.

Table IG9.1 Pandemic Flu Case Overview.

Investigation	Learning Goals	Inquiry Skills Used
Core Investigations		
I. Exploring Flu Antigens, Genetics, and Replication	Introduction to the roles and structures of the H and N viral surface proteins. Students use Chapter 19 to explore the process of antigenic shift and consider the potential for increasing flu variability through this mechanism. Relationship of the viral replication cycle to drug intervention and the role of vaccines in pandemics is investigated.	• making inferences
II. Pandemic Flu (Possible): The Spread of H5N1 Avian Influenza	Students use the three maps provided as a visual data set to begin investigating the spread of H5N1 avian influenza. Students will see how data on the spread of disease in humans, poultry, and wild birds are relevant and that understanding migration patterns may be a clue in understanding the epidemiology of this influenza.	• observing of visual data • detecting patterns • drawing inferences • evaluating various types of map data (static versus interactive) • posing questions • calculating death rates
III. Critical Reading: The Body's Defenses Against the Flu	Students use Chapter 43: The Immune System to relate the mechanisms of the innate and acquired immune system responses to influenza A viruses and also to the ways we stimulate these responses in vaccination.	• making inferences about specifics based on the reading
IV. Internet Activity: Influenza in the Media	This investigation sends students to the Internet to search for media images used by countries in which avian flu has occurred in humans to inform the public about the influenza.	• image searching • evaluating the effectiveness of communication, in terms of both basic biological information and public health messages.
V. Using Data to Explore Pandemic Flu (Past and Possible) Excel tools for data graphing, table making Multiple representations of data	Data from the 1918 pandemic is provided for students to graphically represent and investigate relationships among age, sex, race, location, and flu mortality in 1918. Using human-to-human transmission models, students investigate the effectiveness of mitigations such as vaccination and social distancing.	• graphing data and evaluating methods of data presentation • interpretating output from an Excel-based model of susceptibility, infection, and recovery (SIR) • calculating mortality rates from raw data • making inferences based on data and simulation

Additional Investigations		
VI. Pandemic Planning	A list of issues and concerns being considered by pandemic planners is presented. Students assume a stakeholder perspective to respond to one or more of those issues. Multiple types of student products are suggested.	• communicating scientific information to nonscientists • information searching • developing an argument from a single perspective
VII. Open-Ended Investigations	Students have free access to the SIR model used in Investigation V. They may develop their own scenarios and hypotheses and test them with the model.	• manipulating an Excel-based model • developing and testing hypotheses

Case Narrative

Pandemic Flu (Past): An Oral History by Teamus Bartley, Recorded by Nyoka Hawkins, 1987

T. BARTLEY: . . . You ain't old enough to remember **the year the flu struck the people so bad** in this . . . in this country, do you?

HAWKINS: No.

T. BARTLEY: That was in 1918.

HAWKINS: Yeah, I think that both my . . . both my great-grandparents died in that.

.T. BARTLEY: . . . Yeah, they did. Yeah. It was the saddest looking time then that ever you saw in your life. My brother lived over here in the camps then and I was working over there and . . . I was dropping cars under the tipple. And the fl- . . . that . . . that . . . **epidemic broke out** and **people went to dying** and it was just four **and five every night dying** right there in the camps. Every night. And I began going over there. My brother and hi- . . . all his family took down with it. It . . . **what did they call it?** The flu? Yeah. Eight- . . . **1918 flu**. And when I'd get over there, I'd ride my horse and go over there of a evening, I'd stay with my brother about three hours and do what I could to help them and every one of them was in the bed and sometimes Dr. Preston would come while I was there. He was **the doctor. And he said, "I'm trying to save their lives, but I'm afraid I ain't going to."** They was so bad off.

HAWKINS: _____

T. BARTLEY: And every . . . nearly every porch . . . **every porch that I'd look at had . . . would have a casket box** setting on it. And **men digging graves** just as hard as they could and the mines had to shut down. There wadn't nary a man . . . there wadn't a . . . there wadn't a mine running or a lump of coal running nowhere. . . .

T. BARTLEY: Stayed that a way for about six . . . weeks.

Note: This 1918 flu narrative and others can be found using the OER Commons (Open Educational Resources) website at http://www.oercommons.org.

Suggested Answers for Case Analysis

1. **Recognize potential issues and major topics in the case**. What is this case about? Underline terms or phrases that seem to be important to understanding this case. Then list **3–4** biology-related topics or issues in the case.

Flu of 1918 and its effects on coal mining, high death rates, treatments

2. **What specific questions do you have about these topics?** By yourself, or better yet, in a group, make a list of what you already know that is related to the case in the "What Do I Know?" column. List questions you would like to learn more about in the "What Do I Need to Know?" column.

What Do I Know?	What Do I Need to Know?
• There was a pandemic of flu in 1918. • It killed many people. • It interrupted work; mines closed. • Some people lived in camps. • It lasted about 6 weeks, according to the transcript. • The doctor felt he couldn't help people get better. • Dealing with the dead was a huge issue. • In 1918, World War I was ending. • There were no vaccines then. • Viruses were generally unknown. • Influenza is caused by a virus. • There's a flu shot that you can get every year.	• Did soldiers/sailors bring the flu from elsewhere? • Was there flu in other countries besides the United States? • How long did it last? • What treatments were available then? • What treatments are available now? • How is flu spread? • Why did so many people die of it? • What made this particular flu so deadly? • Do people die of flu today, like the annual flu? • Have there been other epidemics of flu? • Can a pandemic flu happen again?

3. Put a check mark by **1–3** questions or issues in the "What Do I Need to Know?" list that you think are most important to explore.

4. **What kinds of references or resources would help you answer or explore these questions?** Identify two different resources and explain what information each resource is likely to give that will help you answer the question(s). Choose specific resources.

Websites such as that of the World Health Organization, the United Nations, the U.S. Department of Agriculture, the CDC. Research papers or reports of research in scientific journals or in popular publications such as Newsweek or Scientific American. Experts such as local public health workers, physicians, scientists. Historical records of the 1918 flu.

Suggested Answers for Core Investigations

I. Exploring Flu Antigens, Genetics, and Replication

The transcript in the case is an oral history told by a survivor of the deadly flu pandemic (global epidemic) of 1918. It is estimated that this flu was responsible for at least 40 million deaths worldwide. Questions about the 1918 flu and why it was so deadly were unanswered for years. In 1995, scientists successfully sequenced the genome of the virus using archival autopsy tissues of known victims from 1918 (Taubenberger and Morens, 2006). The virulent human-to-human transmissible influenza of 1918 is an avian flu virus that scientists named H1N1. Less lethal descendants of H1N1 are among those causing the seasonal flu for which we get immunizations (vaccinations) each year.

This investigation emphasizes Concepts 19.1, 19.2 (read Reproductive Cycle of Animal Viruses), and 19.3 (read Viral Diseases in Animals and Emerging Viruses), and Table 19.1. Be sure to examine the diagram of the flu virus.

Both H1N1 from 1918 and today's closely monitored avian flu virus, H5N1, are classified as influenza A viruses.

1. What molecule does the H stand for in the name of both viruses, where is the H molecule located on the virus, and what role does the H molecule play in the life cycle of the virus?

   H *stands for hemagglutinin. It is a viral surface protein (envelope protein) that helps the flu virus attach to specific host cells.*

2. What molecule does the N stand for, where is it located, and what is its function in the viral life cycle?

   N *stands for neuraminidase, a viral surface protein (envelope protein) that triggers the breakdown of the endosome in which the virus particle is trapped. This allows the release of viral RNA into the cell. Neuraminidase also helps break down mucus to allow the H to attach to cell receptors.*

The internal structure of influenza A flu viruses includes a matrix surrounding eight individual negative-stranded RNA molecules, each within its own capsid, that make up its viral genome. Each of the RNA strands codes for a specific protein.

3. The virus uses the host cell to produce more copies of itself. As the viral RNA replicates in the host, mutations arise much more frequently in the viral genome than in the host genome (which replicates DNA). Why do more mutations occur in the virus than in the host?

   There is no error checking with RNA replication as in DNA replication.

In addition to mutation (antigenic drift), influenza A viruses can also exchange RNA with other strains of influenza A that may have simultaneously infected the same host cell. The RNA molecules can undergo genetic recombination, producing new strains with unique viral genomes in a process called antigenic shift. New strains of influenza A are produced continuously through both mutation and recombination, necessitating annual seasonal flu shots to prevent infection.

4. Depending on the strain, influenza A is found in a variety of animal hosts including humans, pigs, birds, cats, dogs, or even whales. Many influenza A viruses are not specific for a single kind of animal host. In the discussion that follows, "Pandemic Flu (Possible)," maps showing the current spread of H5N1 include the density of chicken farms and pig farms as well as human populations. Why do you think these three populations are being tracked by epidemiologists looking for new strains of avian flu?

   Pigs are a good mixing ground (antigenic shift) for influenza viruses. They can become coinfected with avian strains and human strains. Looking at the genetic makeup of viruses from the 1918 flu showed that the pandemic form had elements of human, pig, and avian versions of the infective virus. As mammals, pigs have many similarities to humans. If mutations arise allowing infected pigs to transmit the flu easily from pig to pig, that mutation might work for humans or might be a step on the way to a human-to-human strain of the flu. Where bird and pig populations are located and where they are likely to interact are important data in tracking bird-pig-human flu transmission.

5. Suppose a human host suffering from seasonal influenza A (readily transmitted from human to human) comes down with avian flu at the same time. What serious consequences might result?

   If the viruses re-assort so that human-to-human transmission is possible for the deadly avian flu, a new pandemic could begin.

6. The immune system responds specifically to the exact combination of the H and N surface proteins found in a flu virus particle. Currently, 16 antigenically distinct groups of H molecules and 9 distinct groups of N molecules have been identified. How many possible antigenically distinct combinations of H and N could occur?

   There are 16 kinds of H proteins and 9 kinds of N proteins. The possible H and N protein combinations are 16 × 9 or 144 combinations.

Fortunately, not every combination of H and N proteins causes the flu in human hosts. In addition, not all influenza is human-to-human transmissible like the deadly H1N1 flu of 1918. In fact, as of April 2007, the only known human-to-human transmissible influenza A strains include the H1, H2, or H3 proteins combined with the N1 or N2 proteins. These strains are transmitted via virus-laden droplets that are coughed or sneezed into the air or onto surfaces and then contact susceptible tissues.

Other combinations of the H and N proteins cause flu in other species, but they cannot easily initiate disease in humans. The H5N1 "bird" flu is deadly, but it was not known to be human-to-human transmissible at the time this book was published.

When a viral hemagglutinin attaches to a specific receptor on a host cell, it initiates the process by which the virus gains entry into the host cell. Without these receptors, infection cannot occur.

See Table 9.1 for differences in the receptors for H1, H2, and H3 versus H5.

Table 9.1 Comparing Hemagglutinin Receptors in Humans and Birds.

H1, H2, and H3 Human Flu	H5 Avian Flu
Receptors are host cell–surface glycoproteins that terminate in sialic acid linked to the penultimate (next to last) galactose by an alpha 2,6 linkage.	Receptors are host cell–surface glycoproteins whose terminal sialic acid is linked to the penultimate galactose by an alpha 2,3 linkage.
Cells with these glycoproteins are common in the human upper respiratory tract (nose, upper throat).	Cells with these glycoproteins are common in bird upper respiratory tracts.
	Human cells having glycoproteins with the alpha 2,3 linkages are found deeper in the human respiratory tract, throat, and deeper in the lungs.

Table based on information in Kuiken et al., 2006.

7. **a.** Explain how the location of human glycoprotein receptors for H1, H2, and H3 influenza A antigens facilitates transmission of these strains among humans.

    Because these H1, H2, and H3 antigens bind to receptors that are closest to the exterior of humans (eyes, nose, and upper throat), the virus rapidly encounters suitable host cells.

   b. Explain how the location of human glycoprotein receptors for H5 influenza A antigens has contributed to the failure—so far—of this virus to be readily transmitted among humans.

    Because these receptors are deeper inside people, the H5N1 virus has to be breathed in deeply. And because the viruses lodge deeper in the respiratory tract, coughing will not contribute to further spread of the H5N1 virus as much as it does with those viruses establishing themselves in the upper respiratory tract.

8. The World Health Organization Global Influenza Programme is developing "pre-pandemic" candidate vaccines based on H5N1 viruses from infected humans. These pre-pandemic vaccines are needed for preparedness planning and are used in studies that inform dosage, cross-reactivity, and cross-protection. They are also available for governments to request for pilot vaccine production (World Health Organization, 2007).

    Do you think that these pre-pandemic vaccines will be effective against an H5N1 influenza that becomes human-to-human transmissible? Why or why not?

    The H and N antigens are capable of mutation within their antigenic class. Because H5N1 is an RNA-containing virus, such mutations are common. A vaccine produced now against current antigens (those capable of infecting birds but only weakly capable of infecting humans) would be unlikely to be effective against a new strain of avian influenza.

If the H5N1 becomes transmissible human to human, it is very likely that the specific H5 protein required in the vaccine will be a mutation of the H5 protein that isn't capable of human-to-human transmission.

9. A new strain of H5N1 avian flu could emerge that would result in human-to-human transmission.

a. Why is vaccine development not the highest priority right now?

The new strain would be different from what is around right now. Any vaccine made now might not be effective against the new strain. Also, vaccines take months to develop and produce. Further, most vaccines are made using hen eggs and avian influenza kills these. Different methods are being tested for production of vaccine to avian influenza. So, producing a vaccine now would not be a high priority from the perspective of the pharmaceutical companies.

b. Once an epidemic has started, vaccine development will be a high priority. Epidemics often occur in "waves" of illness, with different segments of the population becoming ill each time. Three waves of disease, each lasting weeks, are not rare in a flu epidemic. Why does creating a vaccine in preparation for a second wave of an epidemic make the most sense?

Creating a vaccine for the second wave makes sense because the vaccine would be made against the actual virus forms causing the human-to-human infection. Vaccination is highly effective if the vaccine is the correct one and individuals are inoculated before they encounter the pathogen.

10. Review the replication cycle for flu viruses in Chapter 19. Pharmaceutical companies wish to produce antiviral drug therapies that can interrupt the viral replication cycle while causing minimal adverse effects on the host cells. Several classes of drugs are known to interrupt influenza A replication.

Oseltamivir (Tamiflu) and zanamivir (Relenza) are drugs that inhibit the action of the N protein. Oseltamivir has been used successfully in some cases but only during the first 36–48 hours post-exposure. What part of viral replication is affected by these two drugs? Why is early treatment needed?

The N protein is necessary for the release of completed progeny virus from the infected host cell. Disrupting this stage of viral reproduction will slow down the spread of the virus to uninfected cells in the host. Transmission may also be slowed because the viruses will not be so prevalent in emissions by coughing or sneezing from infected individuals.

11. Resistance of avian influenza A to oseltamivir has already been observed. For example, a resistant H5N1 influenza A mutant has been isolated from a human. There was a substitution of a single amino acid at position 274, in which a tyrosine replaces histidine (deJong et al., 2005). Explain how resistance to a drug increases the fitness of the virus.

If there is a mixed population of viruses, some with resistance to a drug and some without, those with the resistance will be able to reproduce more often than those without, thus increasing the fitness of those viruses with the mutation that confers resistance.

II. Pandemic Flu (Possible): The Spread of H5N1 Avian Influenza

While the 1918 "Spanish flu" pandemic is long over, its lessons have been critical to understanding subsequent flu pandemics (in 1957 and 1968) as well as for preparing for future pandemics. The current H5N1 avian influenza is a different type of flu virus than those that have infected humans in the past. At the time of this publication, H5N1 has been only avian-to-human transmissible, but it is frequently deadly in the people who contract it from birds. In this investigation, you will be making observations from the maps that follow, detecting patterns, and drawing inferences about the occurrence and spread of H5N1 avian influenza.

Use the maps in Figures 9.2a, b, and c to learn more about the H5N1 avian influenza A.

1. Examine Figure 9.2a. In 3–4 sentences, describe the general pattern of H5N1 avian flu that is shown in this map. Tell what continents and approximate latitudes are affected, where the flu seems to be most common in poultry, and where wild birds are the only cases reported so far.

China by far has the most bird flu in poultry, followed by central Russian Federation, India, countries surrounding the Black Sea, Southeast Asia, and Indonesia. Less prevalent areas include Burkina Faso and Nigeria, Egypt, and Saudi Arabia. Lowest prevalence is in Western Europe and the United Kingdom. So far, the virus is reported in equatorial and temperate latitudes. Flu occurs in wild birds only in parts of China, Russia, Turkey, northern Africa, and Europe. These locations have not reported cases of poultry or human infections. (Compare Figures 9.2a and 9.2b for specific locations.)

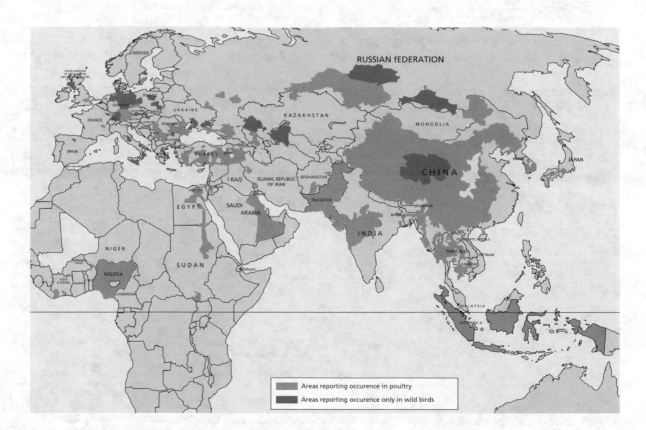

Areas reporting occurence in poultry
Areas reporting occurence only in wild birds

Figure 9.2a Confirmed occurrence of H5N1 avian influenza in poultry and wild birds, March 2003–2007. The horizontal black line is the approximate location of the equator. (*Source:* Adapted from World Health Organization. WHO 2007. All rights reserved.)

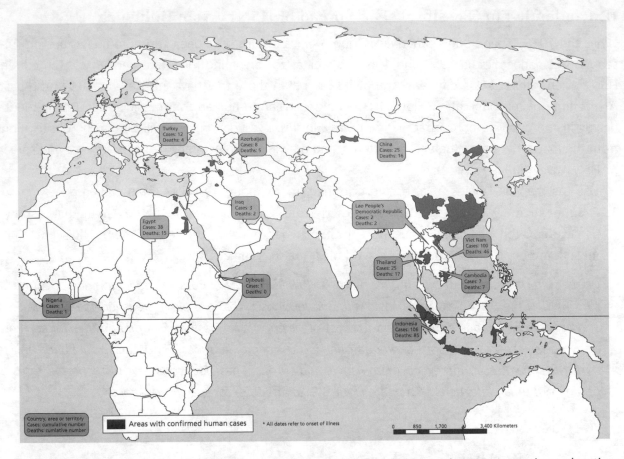

Figure 9.2b Areas with confirmed human cases of avian influenza, 2003–March 2007. Approximate location of equator is shown. (*Source:* Adapted from World Health Organization. © WHO 2007. All rights reserved.)

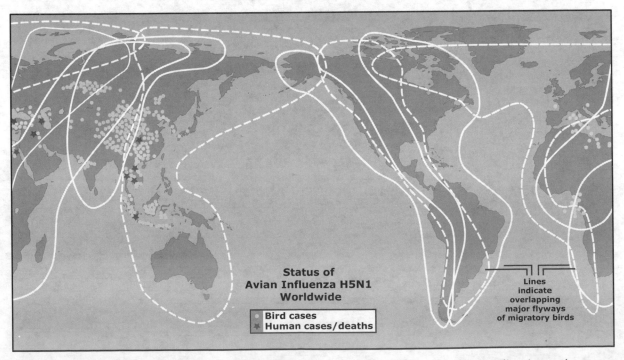

Figure 9.2c Global migration flyways. (*Source:* Adapted from *California Agriculture* online journal. © 2006. The Regents of the University of California)

2. Next examine Figure 9.2b. How does the density of human cases compare with the distribution of the H5N1 flu in poultry? In wild birds?

   The human cases appear to be coincident with the regions where poultry is infected. No cases are shown in areas where the disease is in wild birds only.

3. What inferences can you draw from these data about how avian flu is transmitted to humans? Explain each one, referring to the data you used in developing that inference.

   Answers will vary. Here are three examples.

   Avian flu appears to be transmitted to humans from infected domestic poultry. There are no cases of flu where it is observed to be only in wild birds.

   Having sick poultry alone is insufficient to explain the transmission to humans. For example, see India, which has reported no human disease to date but has reported H5N1 influenza in poultry.

   At this point, it appears that most of the human cases are in tropical or low temperate latitudes. China, for example, has 24 cases spread out over its large poultry producing areas. Vietnam and Indonesia, with higher numbers, are warm tropical climates with high poultry production. Egypt's cases are only where there is poultry production and it is warm there.

4. Update Figure 9.2b with the most recent data from the World Health Organization. Place the new information directly on the map. (Go to the website and search for avian influenza cases. Data in Table 9.2 are from WHO, dated June 7, 2007. http://www.who.int/csr/disease/avian_influenza/country/).

Table 9.2 Incidence of Avian Influenza H5N1 in Humans, April–June 7, 2007.

Country	2007	
	Cases	Deaths
Cambodia	1	1
China	1	1
Egypt	5	1
Indonesia	18	13
Total	25	16

5. Use the updated Figure. 9.2b to calculate the death rate due to bird flu for Indonesia, Vietnam, China, Nigeria, and Egypt.

   Death rate = (number dead/total cases) × 100%. Round to nearest 0.1%.

   Note: These values will change if students look up more recent data.

   Indonesia ___*79.8%*___   Vietnam ___*43%*___ Nigeria ___*100%*___

   China ___*64%*___ Egypt ___*41.2%*___

6. If you were planning a trip to one of the countries listed in number 5, would you rather be told the death rate or the number of cases and deaths in each country? Explain.

I would prefer the raw data of number of cases and deaths because I can use it to calculate the death rate and then have both sets of data. Also, the death rate alone does not tell how prevalent the disease is in that country. For example, although Nigeria had a 100% death rate, it had only two cases total, whereas Vietnam, with a 43% death rate, had the most cases—93. So, the chance of encountering the virus in humans is less in Nigeria than in Vietnam.

7. Egypt reported its first cases of avian influenza in humans in December 2006. In the first 3 months of 2007, there were 14 more human cases of avian flu, with three deaths in that quarter year. Like people in much of the world, most Egyptian households keep small numbers of chickens. However, a tradition unique to Egypt is that their poultry are fed mouth to mouth by women who first chew grain and then blow the powdered feed into the mouths of their birds.

   What does this information further suggest about the ways avian influenza H5N1 spreads to humans? What additional information would you want in order to confirm your idea?

This suggests that close contact with poultry, especially with the mouth, is related to very high rates of infection with the avian flu virus. I would want to know how many of the cases involved women who had been feeding poultry in this way.

8. As you know, many wild birds fly to different parts of the earth as they follow their annual cycles of migration, mating, nesting, and overwintering. Examine the major flyways shown in Figure 9.2c. In a few sentences, describe the patterns you see in these flyways. Include descriptors such as the degree to which they overlap, their general directional orientations, and their extent.

Flyways are oriented mainly over land and generally northeast to southwest (eastern hemisphere) or northwest to southeast (western hemisphere). There is a great deal of overlap along their length, with the most overlap occurring in the northernmost latitudes (tundra). Most of them connect two or more continents. Only two flyways pictured from the eastern hemisphere overlap with those in the western hemisphere.

9. Given what you now know about the location of avian influenza and bird migration, make an inference about where you think this disease is most likely to be first detected in the United States. Explain your reasoning.

It will most likely arrive in Alaska first. The avian flu is more prevalent in the flyway surrounded by dashed black lines that connect Australia, Southeast Asia, China, and western Russia with Alaska. It is also possible that it could arrive on the eastern side of the United States, coming from the flyway that includes western Africa and northern Europe. At present, the avian flu is not very common in this second flyway.

10. From which part of the world do you think avian flu came to Nigeria? Explain.

Most likely from the Turkey-Egypt area. Two flyways connect Nigeria to those regions quite directly. It is possible that birds carried the flu from other regions as there is a great deal of overlap in flyways near Nigeria.

11. Extending this investigation: Visit one of the many interactive maps on avian influenza. Two particularly good ones are offered by the British Broadcasting group in the United Kingdom: http://news.bbc.co.uk/1/shared/spl/hi/world/05/bird_flu_map/html/1.stm and MSNBC: http://www.msnbc.msn.com/id/12375868/from/ET/

    a. Tell which map you viewed and at least two new bits of information you learned.

       BBC map shows (1) the temporal spread of flu in birds and humans and (2) indicates which countries had new infections in each half year.

       MSNBC map shows (1) the temporal spread of flu in flocks of birds and humans and (2) uses a prominent graphic to show the numbers of infections and deaths in humans.

    b. Write two questions that you are able to answer with the information on the interactive map that you could not answer with the static maps provided in this investigation.

       Answers will vary but should include reference to some feature of the interactive maps that is lacking in the static map. For example:

       - *How long did it take for human cases of bird flu to be seen in Africa after they appeared in Turkey?*
       - *How long did it take before human cases of bird flu were seen outside of Asia?*
       - *Does the flu infect humans more in some months than in others?*
       - *Are those months the same at all latitudes?*
       - *Are they the months we would expect to see if bird migration is playing a role?*

III. Critical Reading: The Body's Defenses Against the Flu

Before delving further into this investigative case, you should be familiar with the structure and reproduction of viruses, especially influenza. If you have not already read Chapter 19: Viruses, you should do so now as background.

This Critical Reading is focused mainly on Chapter 43: The Immune System. Read the Overview; Concepts 43.1, 43.2, and 43.3 through Active and Passive Immunization; and in, 43.4, emphasize Acquired Immune System Evasion by Pathogens.

Innate Immunity: All Animals

1. Once a pathogen (a biological agent that causes disease) manages to get past an animal's physical barriers, there is a very good chance that it will be detected by the animal's immune system. At the molecular level, how does an animal detect the presence of a pathogen and determine that it is an intruder and nonself?

   Recognition occurs within the animal's body using molecular receptors that specifically bind to molecules from foreign cells or viruses. These foreign molecules are not found in the animal's body unless it has been invaded.

2. A single virus particle of influenza A is insufficient to initiate disease in humans. It is estimated that between 100 and 1,000 influenza A virus particles are necessary to cause the flu in an individual. A single droplet sneezed from an infected person is likely to contain sufficient virus particles to initiate the disease.

   Explain why a single virus particle is insufficient. To do this, describe both the barrier and the cellular mechanisms of innate immunity that could play a role in stopping viral particles from initiating and then spreading flu within a vertebrate host.

a. *Barrier defenses such as skin, mucous membranes, enzymes in saliva and tears, stomach acid, and secretions on skin that low pH may deactivate or prevent entrance of the virus particles.*

b. *Cellular defenses: phagocytosis and subsequent intracellular degradation by neutrophils, dendritic cells, and macrophages; a few receptors for general classes of nonself pathogen molecules. Chemicals such as interferons produced by infected cells cause nearby cells to produce antiviral toxins or summon macrophages. Proteins of the complement system are also antimicrobial in that, once activated, they cause pathogen cells to burst.*

Fever, clotting, and an increase in phagocytic macrophages found in the inflammatory response may also limit the spread of microbes.

Natural killer cells may attack virus-infected cells, thus limiting the spread of the virus.

A recent summary of clinical findings in people infected with the avian H5N1 influenza A showed that elevated levels of interferons, various interleukins, tumor necrosis factor (TNF), and monocyte attractant protein were higher in patients who died than in those who survived. These strong cellular responses of the innate immune system may actually have contributed to the multi-organ failure and sepsis seen in many patients (WHO Writing Committee, 2005). By elevating the innate immune response to dangerous levels, it appears the H5N1 avian influenza turned the host's innate defenses against the host in some patients, resulting in several deaths.

Acquired Immunity: Vertebrates Only

In vertebrates, once the innate immune response fails to prevent host invasion, the acquired immune response takes over. In contrast to the more general innate immunity, acquired immunity is a response to specific pathogens. Unfortunately, it takes from several days to 2 weeks for the acquired response to be fully effective. Records from the U.S. Navy revealed that when the 1918 flu was diagnosed on any ship, the entire crew was quarantined onboard and virtually all crew members got sick. Many of the men died despite their own immune responses and medical treatment.

3. In the acquired immune response, two types of lymphocytes, B cells and T cells, are the key players.

Review Concepts 43.2 and 43.3 and Figures 43.9 and 43.10.

a. Compare and contrast the antigen receptors of B and T cells.

Both B and T cells have thousands of copies of glycoprotein antigen receptors, all of them identical on a single cell. Both T and B antigen receptors are made of protein subunits that have constant and variable regions, with portions of the constant regions spanning the membrane. B cell receptors are composed of four protein subunits and have two active sites per molecule in the variable regions. (A shortened version of antigen receptor molecules secreted by B cells to the blood are known as antibodies or immunoglobulins. The antibody proteins retain the same active site but lack the transmembrane parts of the protein.) T cell receptors are composed of two protein subunits and have one active site.

b. B and T cells can only recognize antigens when they are in specific locations. Where are the antigens located that B cells can detect?

B cells bind to intact antigens, whether they are connected to the pathogen or floating free.

c. Where are the antigens located that the two kinds of T cells can detect? Include the role of the MHC in your answer.

T cells can bind only to antigen fragments that are presented on the major histocompatability complex (MHC) proteins that have made their way to the surface of host cells. Helper T cells and cytotoxic T cells recognize antigens bound to class II MHC on B cells, dendritic cells, and macrophages. Helper T cells do not kill the cells that present the antigen.

4. Examine Figure 43.16 and focus on the acquired immune system events following first exposure to an antigen. This was the case for the sailors, coal miners, and everyone else infected in 1918.

   a. How are the innate and the acquired immune systems linked? How does one system inform the other of an invasion by a foreign particle?

   At the start of an infection, signals from phagocytic cells carrying out innate immune responses activate lymphocytes, setting the stage for the slower developing acquired response. For example, as macrophages and dendritic cells ingest microbes, these phagocytic cells secrete cytokines, proteins that help recruit and activate lymphocytes. Macrophages and dendritic cells also have a direct role in pathogen recognition by B cells and T cells by "presenting" pathogen antigens on their MHC proteins. The complement system is also involved, as its molecules provide information from the innate to the acquired system.

   b. In the acquired immune response, which cells undergo clonal selection once their receptors have joined with one of the antigens?

   Helper T cells, cytotoxic T cells, and B cells undergo clonal selection once activated by binding to an antigen.

   c. Why is clonal selection a key event in whether or not the acquired immune response is successful?

   Clonal selection means that clones are formed by activated B and T lymphocytes. This rapid proliferation increases the capacity of the acquired immune system to respond to the specific pathogen currently causing infection and/or disease. Further, the clones of B and T cells subsequently differentiate into effector and memory cells.

   d. B plasma cells are effector B cells that fight off the infection differently than cytotoxic T cells do. Explain.

   B plasma cells are those that produce antibodies, which are a form of the antigen receptor lacking the transmembrane portion of the protein. Antibodies attach to the antigen, causing it to be inactivated. In contrast, cytotoxic T cells secrete toxins into infected cells, causing the infected cells to die and thus slowing the replication and spread of the virus within the host.

   e. Although not a factor in disease caused by influenza A, what would be the effect on the acquired immune response if the helper T cells were removed from the system? (The virus causing the current AIDS pandemic targets such T cells.)

   Helper T cells are one way the innate immune system communicates with the acquired immune system. Those phagocytes and dendritic cells that have engulfed a virus present the antigen fragments on their class II MHC proteins. Once a helper T cell binds the antigen, it becomes activated. It begins clonal selection of more helper T cells, both effector and memory types. The helper T cells activate more lymphocytes, both B cells and T cells. Thus, helper T cells also bridge the humoral and cell-mediated parts of the acquired immune response.

5. Immunization against common strains of human-to-human transmissible influenza A is needed every year because the seasonal flu mutates readily. In the case of the 1918 flu, immunization was poorly understood and not available. For a possible H5N1 pandemic, immunization will play a significant role.

In the acquired immune system, how does an immunization protect a person from a disease like flu?

The inoculation stimulates the immune response in the same way that first exposure to an intact pathogen stimulates it. Thus, innate response cells, such as dendritic and macrophage cells, engulf the inoculum, break down the antigen proteins, and present them on their MHC proteins. These are detected by helper T cells, which begin the clonal selection process as well as alerting B cells to the presence of the antigen. B cells also begin clonal selection. The response to inoculation, like that to any first exposure, takes 10–17 days.

The key piece of the protection conferred by a vaccine is that both the T and B cells make memory cells that circulate in the blood stream and lymphatic systems for years. These cells can rapidly detect the pathogenic virus because its antigens are now "known" by the host. Thus, a secondary acquired immune response is possible, allowing the host to mount a large antibody production and cytotoxic T cell production within just a few days.

IV. Internet Activity: Influenza in the Media

The communication of biological information is an essential service for our global society. It is not unexpected that a current concern like the avian flu is frequently reported on in the media, but the 1918 flu is also still in the news.

In early 2007, several articles cited Sir Mark Sykes, a victim of the Spanish flu epidemic, who died at the age of 39 in a hotel room in February 1919 while attending the Paris peace conference following World War I. Because the British diplomat was buried in a sealed lead coffin, researchers were hopeful that well-preserved body samples could be obtained.

1. After the flu virus is retrieved from the diplomat's remains, what is likely to be done with the sample?

Nucleic acid will be extracted from the lung tissues. RT-PCR will be used to isolate and amplify the viral RNA. The RNA will then be sequenced. The sequence data will be compared to other influenza A sequences.

2. Considering that it has been 90 years since the outbreak of the 1918 flu, are you surprised by the current scientific interest? (When is scientific investigation done?)

Some students may find this investigation into the past surprising. Science is never finished as new methods, tools, and questions continue to be developed. As organisms continue to evolve, new investigations into their ancestors may provide information necessary for coping with them.

Note: Interestingly, known samples of the 1918 influenza are represented only by the second wave of the pandemic. There are no known samples of the strain that initiated the first wave.

To consider how current avian flu biology is being communicated globally, you can use a search engine such as Google Image Search to look for images used to communicate with the public in countries where human cases of avian flu have been reported.

3. Choose three images that you feel are helpful in presenting bird flu facts. Record your information in the following chart.

URL	Description	Country

4. What kinds of organizations produce the websites containing the media that you have listed?

   Posters or advertisements are generated by governmental organizations such as departments of public health and agriculture, private pharmaceutical companies, human welfare groups, ministries, and news groups including cartoonists, as well as charlatans advertising cures or activists promoting conspiracy theories.

5. Briefly describe the biological images used and how each relates to the avian flu—for example, a masked and gloved (to prevent viral infection) worker examining poultry (potential carriers of H5N1).

   For this example, images of chickens, the H5N1 virus, human looking worried or ill, well-cooked chicken, iconic representations of death, masked humans, so on.

6. Which of your three media choices would be the most useful for convincing your classmates that avian flu is a real biological concern? Explain.

   Answers will vary, but a good response will identify connections between classmates' lives and prior knowledge with the poster or advertisement chosen. The quality of information and emotional response of the viewer may be mentioned as well.

7. If you were asked to produce a brochure to advise a segment of the public in your country about the risks of avian flu, what group would you select as the target audience? Explain your choice.

   Answers will vary due to interests and might include poultry workers, politicians, teachers, Red Cross volunteers, international travelers, and so on. Look for explanations with rationales such as high-risk population, need for funding research, public education, response in a crisis, and so on.

8. What images would you include in your brochure? Why?

   Images must connect with the specific audience. Rationale might include using H5N1-relevant images such as sick chickens, people working with birds, coughing, and so on. that are familiar and/or compelling. Humor and scare tactics may be offered as rationales as well.

9. Describe at least three examples of biological information you would include for this particular group.

   Answers will vary, but a good answer would include that H5N1 is a new, potentially fatal virus that spreads by contact with birds and bird products. Some students may focus on the threat of a new strain capable of enabling human-to-human transmission.

V. Using Data to Explore Pandemic Flu (Past and Possible)

A. Working with Tables and Graphs on Mortality Statistics

Consider the data in Table 9.3.

Table 9.3 Average Age at Death in the United States, 1911–1919.

Year	Male	Female
1911	50.9	54.4
1912	51.5	55.9
1913	50.3	55
1914	52	56.8
1915	52.5	56.8
1916	49.6	54.3
1917	48.4	54
1918	36.6	42.2
1919	53.5	56

Adapted from *Life Expectancy in the USA, 1900–98* (Noymer, 2007).

1. In 1915, a man could expect to live for <u>*52.5*</u> years. In 1918, this dropped to <u>*36.6*</u>.

2. Between 1917 and the onset of the influenza pandemic in 1918, both male and female life expectancy dropped <u>*11.8*</u> years.

3. Construct a graph with 1911 to 1919 on the *x*-axis and 0 to 60 years of age on the *y* axis. Show separate male and female life expectancy lines by connecting the points plotted for each year versus expected age at death.

   Provide a suitable title for your graph.

   Two examples of titles are Male and Female Life Expectancy from 1911 to 1919, and Average Age at Death for Men and Women in the United States from 1911 to 1919.

4. Which is more effective at quickly conveying the impact of the 1918 influenza pandemic, the table or your graph? Why?

   The graph visually emphasizes the decrease in life expectancy for both males and females in 1918.

Now look at Table 9.4.

Table 9.4 U.S. Deaths per 100,000 Attributed to Influenza and Pneumonia, During 1917–1918.

Age	1917	1918
<1	2,944.5	4,540.9
1–4	422.7	1,436.2
5–14	47.9	352.7
15–24	78	1,175.7
25–34	117.7	1,998
35–44	193.2	1,097.6
45–54	292.3	686.8

Adapted from *Age-Specific Death Rates (per 100,000), Influenza & Pneumonia, USA* (Noymer, 2007).

5. Which age group had the highest number of influenza- and pneumonia-related deaths in 1917?

   Age < 1   In 1918?   *Age < 1*

6. Another way of looking at the data is to consider the specific increase in the number of influenza- and pneumonia-related deaths in one age group between 1917 and 1918. You can calculate this by dividing the number of deaths in 1918 by the number of deaths in 1917. For instance, if you look at the age group < 1 year, divide the number of deaths in 1918 (4,540.9) by the number of deaths in 1917 (2,944.5). The increase in deaths during 1918 is approximately 1.5 times the 1917 deaths.

   How many times greater is the 1918 death total than the 1917 death total for 5- to 14-year-olds?

   352.7 deaths divided by 47.9 deaths equals an overall rate of increase of approximately 7.4 times the 1917 total.

7. Which two age groups experienced the highest increase in the number of influenza- and pneumonia-related deaths between 1917 and 1918?

   15–24 and 25–34.

a. How many times greater is the 1918 total than the 1917 total for each of these two groups?

15.1 times and 17.0 times, respectively.

b. If you were the same age you are now, how much more likely would you have been to succumb from an influenza- or pneumonia-related death in 1918 than in 1917?

Answers depend on the age of the student, but 15.1 times or 17.0 times are the most likely responses for students age 18 or 19.

8. Scientists were puzzled why the 1918 flu resulted in increased deaths in specific age groups. What was so unexpected?

In most diseases, the very young and the very old have the highest mortality, but in this case the usually more healthy younger adult population was affected the most.

B. Working with a SIR Model to Investigate Avian Influenza H5N1

Models help investigators ask questions as well as predict possible outcomes. In this activity, you will use an Excel model (Weisstein, 2007) to simulate disease spread throughout a population. The model divides the host population into three categories:

- susceptible individuals (*S*)
- infected individuals (*I*)
- individuals who have recovered from infection (*R*)

This SIR model produces graphs that track movement into, out of, and between the S, I, and R categories over time. Careful observation enables you to consider how the disease interacts with its host populations. (*Note:* Each disease being modeled is based on specific characteristics that the model user sets.)

Scenario 1

Consider the following simulation results (Figure 9.3) based on a hypothetical scenario in which four poultry workers from Tennessee infected with an H5N1 strain are moved to a health facility with a population of 180.

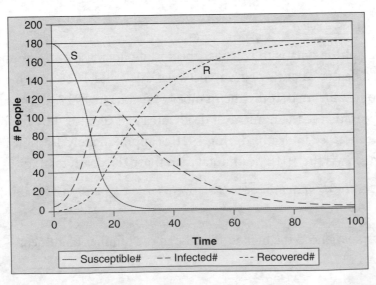

Figure 9.3 Simulation results for Scenario 1 of avian influenza.

1. Is this more likely to be a strain of the virus that is transmitted only from avian to human or a strain that is transmitted from human to human? Explain.

   Human-to-human transmission must be occurring because birds are unlikely to be present at a health facility.

2. About how many individuals remained healthy? What is the transmission rate in this model? Transmission = (R) recovered / (S) susceptible

   All individuals got the disease. The transmission rate is 180/180 or 100%.

3. All infected individuals (I) eventually become recovered individuals (R). What does this tell us about the severity of the viral disease in this model—that is, what is the mortality rate observed here?

   Mortality is zero because all recovered. In this model, the flu is not fatal.

Scenario 2

This is the same hypothetical situation except that 40 people are isolated in a special ward at the facility before they can be exposed to the avian influenza strain.

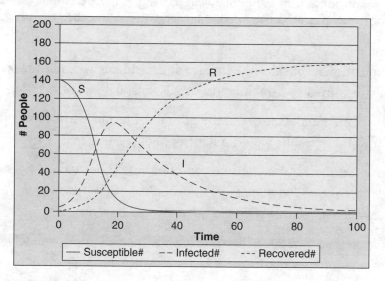

Figure 9.4 Simulation results for Scenario 2 of avian influenza.

4. The number of infected individuals (I) on Day 20 in Scenario 2 (see Figure 9.4) is <u>90</u> as compared to the number of infected individuals (I) on Day 20 in Scenario 1 (see Figure 9.3), which is <u>120</u>.

5. The total number of recovered individuals (R) in Scenario 2 is <u>145</u> as compared to <u>180</u> in Scenario 1. What does this tell us about the efficacy of isolation in this model?

   Isolation provides protection from the virus.

Scenario 3

In 1918, no one knew what caused influenza and vaccines were not available. Nevertheless, it was understood that coughing and sneezing contributed to the spread of the disease. At that time, Seattle public health officials required all passengers and employees of mass transit systems to wear masks (Figure 9.5). Spitting was also prohibited in many cities.

Figure 9.5 Street car conductor in Seattle not allowing passengers aboard without a mask. Record held at: National Archives at College Park, Maryland. Record number 165-WW-269B-11.

In the following simulations, consider the impact of individuals wearing masks during exposure to H1N1. These simulations involve a population of 200 hospital workers.

6. Predict generally what you'd expect to see in the SIR model results with respect to S, I, and R individuals. (Consider how these results would differ from not wearing masks.)

If all the individuals wore masks, the transmission rates would decrease. Fewer individuals would become infected with the flu, so the number of susceptible (S) individuals would remain higher while the number of infected (I) and recovered (R) individuals would be reduced.

In the following simulations, let's reduce the transmission rate to approximately 10% of its previous value once the hospital initiates mask use. Exactly *when* the hospital starts using masks can dramatically affect the course of the epidemic, as the graphs in Figures 9.6 through 9.8 show.

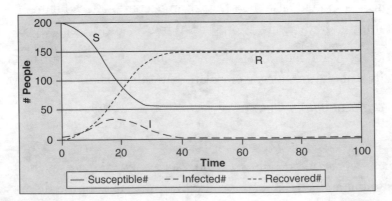

Figure 9.6 Simulation results for Scenario 3 of avian influenza, with masks used starting on day 30, when the epidemic has already nearly run its course.

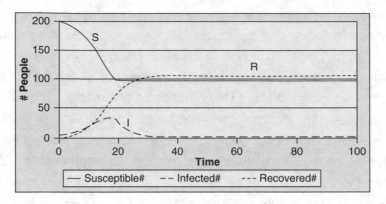

Figure 9.7 Simulation results for Scenario 3 of avian influenza, with masks used starting on day 20, when the epidemic is at its peak.

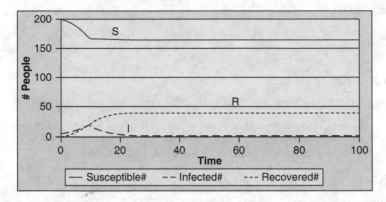

Figure 9.8 Simulation results for Scenario 3 of avian influenza, with masks used starting on day 10, when the epidemic is still in its growth phase.

7. Using your observations of Figures 9.6 through 9.8, defend a policy that makes wearing masks mandatory during the early days of an epidemic such as the 1918 flu.

The answers may vary, but a good answer will address the number of recovered individuals in the day 30, 20, and 10 results. The fewer individuals that have been infected prior to the mask policy being put in place, the lower the number who will become infected.

Suggested Answers for Additional Investigations
VI. Pandemic Planning

While the H5N1 avian influenza A strain may not be the next virus that causes an epidemic around the globe, its severity and high mortality rate in humans have raised the level of alert. Pandemics occur somewhat regularly and planning is ongoing. International cooperative groups are already planning responses to a flu pandemic. At the same time, planning is proceeding at national, state, and local levels.

Planning for a pandemic is complex and involves the participation of many stakeholder groups that have overlapping areas of concern and expertise. A list follows of some of the concerns and issues that need to be addressed in pandemic planning—in this case, for avian influenza.

Address one or more of these concerns from the perspective of one of the following stakeholder groups: public health (including CDC and WHO); medicine-pharmacology; media and public information; agriculture; local, state, and national governing bodies; departments of state; and consumers and taxpayers.

Your instructor may ask you to write a paper, prepare an informational poster or a 30-second radio spot informing the public, conduct a simulated pandemic planning meeting, or prepare some other form of response to these issues and perspectives.

1. Surveillance and monitoring of human and avian cases

2. Fostering international scientific collaboration

3. Developing international cooperation in limiting spread, defining acceptable enforcement

4. Prevention, limiting spread, and ethics

   a. Pharmacologic interventions—efficacy, availability, compliance

      i. Vaccination

      ii. Antivirals as prophylactics

   b. Nonpharmacologic interventions (NPIs)—efficacy and gaining compliance

      i. Community mitigation (school closures, restrictions on movements)

      ii. Quarantine and isolation of healthy and sick individuals

      iii. Travel restrictions locally and globally

      iv. Social distancing

      v. Use of masks and increased hygiene

5. Treatment and ethics

   a. Antiviral availability

   b. Hospital space limitations for isolation and treatment

6. Disposal of bodies if pandemic is extreme

7. Continuation of governance during a pandemic

8. Delivery of services when many are sick—priorities and ethics

   a. Water, food, energy

   b. Workforce reductions due to illness

9. Economic impact (short term) and ethics

   a. Confined animal feeding operations (CAFOS)—placement and regulation

   b. Importers and exporters of other goods and services

   c. Pharmaceutical industry

   d. Health insurance industry

   e. Health care industry

10. Long-term effects on affected countries and ethics
   a. Economic effects
   b. Loss of personnel to pandemic

Some Suggested Resources Related to Pandemic Planning

- Pandemicflu.gov
- Avianflu.gov
- National Governor's Association document on Preparing for Pandemic Influenza http://www.nga.org/Files/pdf/0607PANDEMICPRIMER.PDF (note, this is a large file)
- Centers for Disease Control and Prevention (http://www.cdc.gov/flu/avian)
- World Health Organization (www.who.int/en/)

VII. Open-Ended Investigations

The Excel-based SIR model used in Investigation V is freely available online at http://bioquest.org/icbl/casebook/avian. Consider developing your own scenarios (more virulent flu, different mitigation efforts, etc.) and seeing their effectiveness on the spread of disease.

References

deJong, Menno D , Tran Tan Thanh, Truong Huu Khanh, Vo Minh Hien, Gavin J. D. Smith, Nguyen Vinh Chau, Bach Van Cam, Phan Tu Qui, Do Quang Ha, Yi Guan, J. S. Malik Peiris, Tran Tinh Hien, and Jeremy Farrar. 2006. Oseltamivir resistance during treatment of influenza A (H5N1) infection. *NEJM* 353(25): 2667–2672.

Hawkins, Nyoka. 14 June 1987. Teamus Bartley interview, Appalachia Oral History Project, Louie B. Nunn Center for Oral History, University of Kentucky Libraries, Accession No. 87OH191 App 114.

Kuiken, Thijs, Edward C. Holmes, John McCauley, Guus F. Rimmelzwaan, Catherine S. Williams, and Bryan T. Grenfell. 21 April 2006. Host species barriers to influenza virus infections. *Science* 312(5772): 394–397.

Noymer, Andrew. 2007. Raw data set: Age specific death rates (per 100,000). *Influenza and Pneumonia, USA.* Available online (April 2007) at http://www.demog.berkeley.edu/~andrew/1918/figure1.html

Taubenberger, Jeffery K., and David M. Morens. 2006. 1918 influenza: The mother of all pandemics. *Emerging Infectious Diseases* 12(1), January 2006. Online at http://www.cdc.gov/ncidod/EID/vol12no01/05-0979.htm.

Weisstein, Anton E. 2007. SIR modeling. In *Biological ESTEEM: Excel Simulations and Tools for Exploratory, Experiential Mathematics.* http://bioquest.org/esteem

World Health Organization. 2007. Antigenic and genetic characteristics of H5N1 viruses and candidate H5N1 vaccine viruses developed for potential use as pre-pandemic vaccines. March 2007. Online at http://www.who.int/csr/disease/avian_influenza/guidelines/h5n1virus/en/index.html

The Writing Committee of the World Health Organization (WHO) Consultation on Human Influenza A/H5. 2005. Avian influenza A (H5N1) infection in humans. *NEJM* 353(13):1374–1385.

Maps

Figure 9.2a: http://gamapserver.who.int/mapLibrary/Files/Maps/Global_SubNat_H5N1inAnimal
ConfirmedCUMULATIVE_20070329.png

Figure 9.2b: http://gamapserver.who.int/mapLibrary/Files/Maps/Global_H5N1inHumanCUMULATIVE_
FIMS_20070329.png

Figure 9.2c: http://calag.ucop.edu/0603JAS/images/avianMap.jpg

Chapter 10:

Shh: Silencing the Hedgehog Pathway

INSTRUCTOR'S GUIDE

As with all the cases in this book, please read the preface, if you have not already done so. In the preface you will find suggestions about using Investigative Case–Based Learning (ICBL) in different instructional situations such as starting a new lecture topic, assessing what students already know, setting a context for lab activities, and so on. The preface also describes ways to use cases in a variety of classroom settings and suggests multiple ways to assess learning with cases.

Shh: *Silencing the Hedgehog Pathway* emphasizes materials found in Chapter 11: Cell Communication, Chapter 18: Regulation of Gene Expression, and Chapter 20: DNA Technology and Genomics of Campbell and Reece's *Biology*, 8th edition. The case is about the hedgehog signaling pathway, which plays vital roles in both embryonic development and in the formation of several types of cancers. The hedgehog signaling pathway is one that affects cell division. This case refers directly to information from a peer-reviewed research paper on an antagonist to the hedgehog pathway and its role in reducing basal cell carcinoma. There are four strands in this chapter:

- Cyclopamine, cell signaling and cancer
- Evolution of the hedgehog gene family
- Stem cells and cell signaling
- Antibodies as research tools

The students should complete the Case Analysis immediately following the reading of the case. We strongly suggest that students work in groups to complete the Case Analysis. Actively listening to and challenging the ideas of others can help learners become aware of their own misconceptions, yet value their own and others' prior knowledge.

Five investigations accompany *Shh: Silencing the Hedgehog Pathway*. Four are "core" investigations relating directly to the facts of the case, and one "additional" open-ended investigation extends beyond the facts of the case. Table IG10.1 describes what students will gain from each investigation.

Table IG10.1 Shh: Silencing the Hedgehog Pathway Overview.

Investigation	Learning Goals	Inquiry Skills Used
Core Investigations		
I. Critical Reading: Cell Signaling Pathways	Students use the text to define cancer. Then they use Chapter 11 to apply concepts of cell communication and signaling pathways to the hedgehog signaling pathway. They relate the findings from the paper presented in the case to the function of the hedgehog pathway.	• making inferences • using a model to infer processes • applying general concepts to specific information • graph reading and figure interpretation
II. Phylogenetics of the Hedgehog Gene Family	Students review two text figures, a phylogram and an ultrametric tree based on *hedgehog* gene, and answer questions about phylogenetic relatedness among animal groups. They use conserved gene sequences to determine hedgehog protein relatedness.	• reading trees as hypotheses • using sequence data to infer relationships • recognizing relationships among animal taxa
III. Critical Reading: Stem Cells and Gene Expression	The hedgehog signaling pathway is used to explain how gene expression is regulated in stem cells. Usefulness of stem cell research is demonstrated in understanding development, cell signaling, and treatments for diseases and injuries.	• extending understanding of differential gene expression • differentiating between embryonic and adult cells • considering the usefulness of stem cell research in treatment of diseases and injuries
IV. Investigating the Hedgehog Pathway: Antibodies as Research Tools	Students examine how antibody techniques for immunohistochemistry and Western blots can be used to gain understanding of the hedgehog pathway. They consider and then provide a rationale for the use of a specific antibody.	• applying concepts of antibody specificity into a research problem • giving rationale for experimental design defending methods and materials • drawing conclusions from experimental data
Additional Investigation		
V. Open-Ended Investigations	Students develop a proposal for research on the hedgehog pathway after exploring a curated database of research. Proposal review panels may be an optional activity.	• navigating a complex database • developing an experimental design • writing a proposal • reviewing a proposal

Case Narrative

"I'm so relieved," Ann said as she plopped down in the coffee shop booth where her friend Delores was reading e-mail on her laptop.

"Oh Ann!? What did the doctor say?" Delores asked.

"Well, I do have **skin cancer**, but it's **not melanoma**. It's **basal cell something**. Anyway, it's very **common and easy to treat**," Ann reassured her.

"Is it **genetic**?" Delores asked, "Or does it have something to do with that nice tan you showed off during your teens and twenties?"

"Well **no one else in the family has had skin cancer**." Grimacing, Ann added,"It's more likely I'm **paying for my tan**."

After Ann left, Delores searched for "basal cell cancer" on the Web. She wondered how her friend ended up with skin cancer. She found a **2004 paper by Athar** and colleagues that explored **BCC (basal cell carcinoma)** and the effect of **UV radiation**. BCC, the most common kind of cancer, was linked to problems with the **hedgehog signaling pathway**. Exposure to **UV radiation was one way to impact the pathway.**

"More questions than answers," Delores sighed. She looked up "hedgehog signaling pathway" in **Wikipedia**. She found that this pathway **controls cell division** and is **important in early development**. The pathway was first discovered in fruit flies with a mutation that made them shorter and especially bristly. The researcher thought the fly larvae looked like hedgehogs.

Delores returned to the Athar article. The researchers divided mice into two groups and then exposed them to UV radiation. One group was given a drug called **cyclopamine, a known antagonist to the hedgehog pathway**, in their drinking water, and the other group got plain water. The mice that got the **cyclopamine had many fewer BCCs** at the end of the experiment.

"**I wonder if they will give Ann cyclopamine for her BCC**?" Delores thought as she closed her laptop.

Suggested Answers for Case Analysis

1. **Recognize potential issues and major topics in the case.** What is this case about? Underline terms or phrases that seem to be important to understanding this case. Then list **3–4** biology-related topics or issues in the case.

Hedgehog signaling pathway   *UV radiation*

Cancer: Basal Cell Carcinoma   *Cyclopamine*

Antagonists

2. **What specific questions do you have about these topics?** By yourself, or better yet, in a group, make a list of what you already know that is related to the case in the the "What Do I Know?" column. List questions you would like to learn more about in "What Do I Need to Know?" column.

What Do I Know?	What Do I Need to Know?
Students are likely to mention some or all of these, many of which come from the case:	• *What is the hedgehog signaling pathway?*
	• *Where is it?*
• *BCC is the most common type of cancer.*	• *How does the hedgehog pathway cause cancer?*
• *It occurs on the skin.*	• *Does the hedgehog pathway cause all cancers?*
• *It can be induced by UV.*	
• *UV is a type of radiation from the sun.*	• *How does the hedgehog pathway work?*
• *It is also in tanning beds.*	• *Does the hedgehog pathway do anything else?*
• *With the ozone hole, there is more UV radiation.*	• *What is an antagonist in a biological context?*
• *The hedgehog signaling pathway is involved in BCC.*	• *What is cyclopamine?*
	• *Where does cyclopamine come from?*
• *Cyclopamine is the antagonist to the hedgehog signaling pathway.*	• *How did the scientists know to use it?*
	• *Does it work on other cancers as well?*
• *Antagonism means "going against."*	• *How does it work?*
• *Mice were used as the test animal in the study of cyclopamine.*	• *Can humans be treated with cyclopamine?*
	• *What is the process for making an experimental drug available to the general public?*
• *Cyclopamine reduced the number of BCCs in the mice*	• *What is UV?*
• *Some students may have personal experience with cancer in themselves or their family members and may know about oncogenes. Oncogenes are not the focus of this case. BCC can be treated, usually by surgery.*	• *Is UVA or UV or are both responsible for BCC?*
	• *How does UV induce BCC?*
	• *Is BCC treatable? Survivable?*
	• *Why are mice used? Are they a good system for studying cancer?*
	• *Could this have been done without animals being used?*

- *Most people who have it do not die from it*
- *Melanoma is also a type of skin cancer (this case is not about melanoma).*

- *How close a match are mouse and human mechanisms for using cyclopamine and for causing BCC with UV?*
- *What do these results with a mouse mean for me as a human?*
- *Are any of these genes proto-genes?*
- *Is Wikipedia a good source?*
- *Is the Athar paper a reputable source if she found it on the Internet?*

3. Put a check mark by **1–3** questions or issues in the "What Do I Need to Know?" list that you think are most important to explore.

4. What kinds of references or resources would help you answer or explore these questions? Identify two different resources and explain what information each resource is likely to give that will help you answer the question(s). Choose specific resources.

Students might look up the Athar et al. paper, use websites on cancer at NIH or other places including Wikipedia, talk with people they know who have had BCC or other cancer, talk with a doctor, or use their text.

Suggested Answers for Core Investigations

I. Critical Reading: Cell Signaling Pathways

You should be familiar with the structure and function of proteins that have active sites, such as enzymes or antibodies. To complete this investigation you should read Chapter 11: Cell Communication (specifically, Concepts 11.1 and 11.4) and Chapter 18: Regulation of Gene Expression (specifically, Concepts 18.4 and 18.5).

1. What is cancer? (Hint: Use of multiple sources for this definition, such as Cancerquest [http://www.cancerquest.org] in addition to the text, is recommended.)

Cancer is a disease in cells in which control of cell division becomes unregulated. A mass of dividing cells (tumor) can be produced that can be either benign or malignant. When malignant, it is called cancer. Cells from the mass may metastasize, that is, spread into other parts of the body.

2. What are some of the causes of cancer?

Cancer has many causes, including mutations caused by environment (e.g., nicotine, UV rays), as well as genetic defects in cell cycle control mechanisms, in cell signaling pathways, or activation of proto-oncogenes.

3. Interpret the graph in Figure 10.2 by answering the following questions.

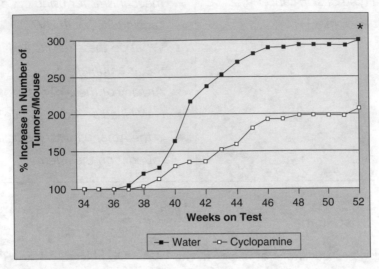

Figure 10.2 Effect of cyclopamine on BCC tumor formation in UVB-irradiated mice. (After Athar et al., 2004) (*Note:* The asterisk means the differences between the two treatments are statistically significant.)

a. On the basis of the shape of the curves, explain the patterns of tumor production in control and experimental mice in weeks 34–52.

For control mice, a sigmoid-shaped curve is shown, in which cancer production is slow between weeks 34–39. Between weeks 39 and 41, there was rapid production of tumors with a slowing of rate between weeks 42 and 46. There was no further increase in tumors until week 52.

For mice given cyclopamine, there is little or no increase in tumors from weeks 34 to 39. A slow but steady increase in rate of tumor production is seen between weeks 40 and 46. Little subsequent increase in tumors is seen after week 47. This is also a sigmoid curve but much flatter.

b. What is the overall percentage increase in tumors for control versus experimental mice?

Overall, a 300% increase in tumor production for water-treated control mice.

Overall, approximately a 200% increase in number of tumors per treated mouse.

4. Use Figure 10.3 to answer the next two questions.

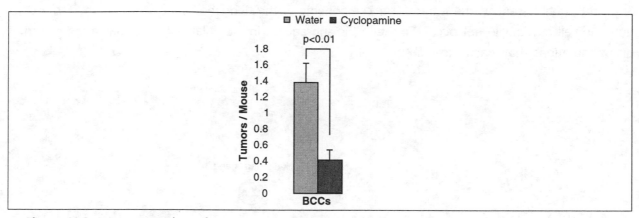

Figure 10.3 Average number of tumors per irradiated mouse with and without cyclopamine (After Athar et al., 2004)

a. How effective was cyclopamine in treating BCC in the mice?

The mice that received water, the controls, visibly have many more tumors than those treated with cyclopamine. So, cyclopamine does not prevent all tumors, but it does reduce the number.

In C, cyclopamine treated mice averaged .4 tumors per mouse, while controls had 1.4 tumors per mouse. This is statistically significant at the p less than or equal to 0.01.

b. Which of these two data formats would be more effecting in presenting the results of the experiment to the public? Which would be more effective for other scientists?

Figure 10.3, the bar graph, might be more effective for the public. Scientists would appreciate the precision of the numbers in Figure 10.2 more than the summary shown in the bar graph and would more fully understand the meaning of the statistical difference between the two treatments.

The hedgehog signaling pathway plays a crucial role in the development of many animal embryos. In addition, the hedgehog pathway controls regeneration of short-lived adult tissues, such as those in skin and blood. When the hedgehog pathway is active, transcription of proteins occurs in target cells followed by rapid division of those cells. The hedgehog pathway is also active in BCC and several other cancers.

The *hedgehog* gene family codes for signaling proteins that serve as ligands binding to receptors in nearby target cells. These proteins activate the hedgehog pathway in the target cells. The hedgehog pathway in the target cells has two membrane proteins named Patched (Ptch) and Smoothened (Smo), as well as several intracellular proteins.

When Shh (Sonic hedgehog) ligand binds to Ptch, then Smo is activated, the signal is transduced, and transcription and cell division result. In the absence of the hedgehog signaling protein, Ptch inhibits Smo, no signal is sent to the intracellular components of the hedgehog pathway, and thus transcription and cell division do not occur. Smo and the subsequent intracellular pathway may also be turned on by mutations that inactivate Ptch.

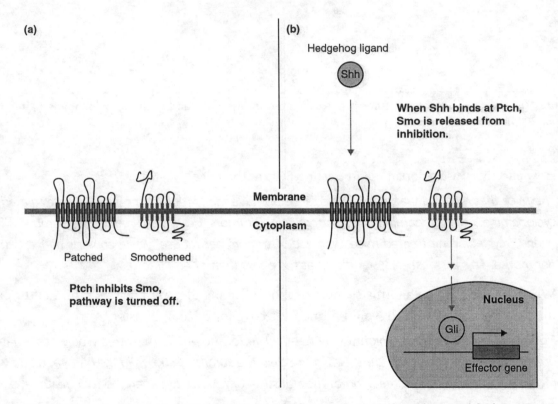

Figure 10.4 Schematic diagram of the hedgehog signaling pathway in vertebrates. (a) The target cell without the hedgehog ligand. Patched and Smoothened are transmembrane proteins embedded in the plasma membrane. Patched inhibits Smoothened and the pathway is turned off. (b) When the hedgehog ligand Shh joins with Patched, Smoothened is released from inhibition and the pathway is turned on. (Weitzman, 2002)

5. Is the hedgehog signaling pathway a local or long-distance type of signaling? Explain.

   It is a local signal. Nearby cells secrete the hedgehog ligand protein. It is not carried in blood, like hormones are, nor is it electrical.

6. Examine Figure 10.4 and identify which molecules are involved in reception, transduction, and response in the hedgehog pathway.

   Ptch and Smo are involved in reception of the hedgehog signal. Gli molecules are involved in transduction. Response is carried out by the effector gene.

7. The mechanism of the activation of Smo by the hedgehog ligand binding to Ptch is not completely understood. However, the model shown in Figure 11.11 in the text shows a pathway with two membrane proteins, similar to the arrangement of membrane proteins in the hedgehog pathway. In this model, cell signaling is involved when the ligand binds to the first receptor protein, activating the G protein. The G protein then activates the second membrane protein, which transduces the signal to the interior of the cell. Explain how this mechanism might be applied to the two membrane proteins in the hedgehog signaling pathway.

   For hedghog, two membrane proteins are involved. When hedgehog binds to Ptch, perhaps some second molecule is activated which binds to Smo, thus activating Smo.

8. As scientists evaluate new data, they frequently have to revise their models. Because we know that Ptch is an inhibitor of Smo and G protein is not involved, revise the model in Figure 11.11 to incorporate this new information.

   Because Smo can become active when Ptch is disabled by mutation, it suggests that the mechanism is different from that shown in Figure 11.11. In Figure 11.11, a signal is required to activate an intermediate molecule (the G protein) that in turn activates the second membrane protein.

   In the hedgehog pathway, the disabling of a molecule (Ptch) allows the second membrane protein to function. This suggests that the mechanism for normal Ptch is involved in inhibiting Smo. The hedgehog ligand changes Ptch to somehow prevent the inhibition. This could be a direct effect of one protein upon the other (Ptch and Smo) or it might involve intermediate molecules. Ptch would affect molecules that inhibit Smo. When bound to hedgehog or when mutated, Ptch could no long affect such molecules, thus releasing the inhibition.

9. Cyclopamine is a known antagonist of Smo. Describe how cyclopamine reduces the number of BCCs in UV-irradiated mice.

   Smo activates the interacellular components of the hedgehog pathway resulting in transcription and subsequent cell division. It does this when hedgehog is present or when stch is absent or mutated. If BCC is present, then the hedgehog pathway is active, meaning that hedgehog is present and Smo is active. If cyclopamine can interfere with Smo, then the cancerous cell division can be stopped or slowed resulting in fewer BCCs.

   The hedgehog signaling pathway is active in the early embryo during development of the neural tube, motor neuron specification, left-right symmetry, body plan, limbs, and retinas (Matlack et al. 2006).

   In the 1950s, sheep feeding on the corn lily (Veratrum spp.) in mountain pastures gave birth to a number of lambs with only one eye. The number of cyclopean lambs (named for the one-eyed Cyclops of Greek mythology) were explained when the compound later named cyclopamine was discovered in the corn lily. To see an image of cyclopia in sheep, go to http://teratology.org/jfs/Natural-Teratogens.html.

10. Explain how a failure to have cell division occurs at a critical time during development could lead to lambs with one eye. See Section 18.4 on critical events in the development of left-right symmetry and body plan.

    The hedgehog genes help determine left-right symmetry and the body plan. A failure of the hedgehog pathway to function can lead to a unilateral structure such as a single eye.

II. Phylogenetics of the Hedgehog Gene Family

Nobel Prize researchers Christiane Nüsslein-Volhard and Eric Wieschaus investigated fruitfly mutations in order to make sense of the role of genes active in the development of fly embryos. They mutated one gene—later named *"hedgehog"*—that resulted in dense spines in shortened fly larvae.

Homologous hedgehog genes were later discovered in vertebrates. After these genes were sequenced in several different kinds of animals, they were compared and used to determine phylogenetic relatedness. If you have not yet studied phylogenetic classification, you may want to read Chapter 26 before completing this investigation. Consider the phylogram in Figure 26.12 in your text as you answer the following questions.

1. What species is used as the outgroup for the *hedgehog* gene in this phylogram? Provide a reason for using this species.

   The fruit fly, Drosophila, has the hedgehog gene and makes a good outgroup because this genus is not considered to be closely related to any of the other organisms in the figure. Note that Drosophila is roughly the same phylogenetic distance from all of the vertebrates.

2. What does the phylogram tell us about the *hedgehog* gene in mammals and birds as compared to the *hedgehog* gene in mammals and amphibians?

   Mammals and birds share a more closely related form of the gene with each other than mammals do with amphibians.

Consider the ultrametric tree in Figure 26.13 in your text as you answer the following questions.

3. Does this ultrametric tree provide information about the rate of change in the *hedgehog* gene for these animal groups? If not, what information can be inferred from this tree?

   Nothing can be inferred about the rate. Based on data from the fossil record, ultrametric trees are used to show time points for common ancestors of these groups.

4. List all the pairs of animal groups that share a more recent common ancestor than humans and birds.

   Humans and rats. Humans and mice. Rats and mice.

The field of developmental biology is changing as scientists use molecular and biological approaches to investigate evolution questions. Since the discovery of classes of conserved regulatory genes or *Hox* genes, the new phrase "evo devo" has been used to refer to the science of evolutionary developmental biology. (See Concept 21.6 in your text.)

5. How could phylogenetic and ultrametric trees help inform researchers interested in designing experiments to study the hedgehog pathway?

   In addition to their value in evolutionary biology, comparative genomic studies confirm the relevance of research on simpler organisms to our understanding of biology in general and human biology in particular. Conservation of genes such as hedgehog suggests the gene plays a role in the development and health of animals. Both the phylogram and ultrametric trees show that. Research using organisms other than humans has resulted in significant medical applications for human health.

After viewing the *hedgehog* phylogram in Figure 26.12, two researchers decide to look more closely at the relationship between hedgehog proteins found in animals. They obtain sequence information from two invertebrates and two vertebrates and choose to limit their study to a portion of the hedgehog protein produced by a highly conserved region of the *hedgehog* gene. The hedgehog proteins were produced by the gene *Hh* (hedgehog) in invertebrates and *Shh (sonic hedgehog)* in vertebrates.

The following amino acid sequences were produced from a conserved region of a gene in the *hedgehog* family of genes.

```
Scorpion Hh   DGPHAINSLH   YEGRAVDITT   SDRDRSKYGM   LARLAVDAGF   DWVYYESRAH   IHCSVKSESA
Human Shh     DGHHSEESLH   YEGRAVDITT   SDRDRSKYGM   LARLAVEAGF   DWVYYESKAH   IHCSVKAENS
Octopus Hh    QGHHAPTSLH   YEGRAVDITT   SDRVRSRYGM   LARLAVEAGF   DWVYYESRSH   IHCSVRSDSL
Chicken Shh   DGHHSEESLH   YEGRAVDITT   SDRDRSKYGM   LARLAVEAGF   DWVYYESKAH   IHCSVKAENS
```

6. Which of these organisms are invertebrates and to what phylum does each belong?

   The invertebrates are the scorpion, an arthropod, and the octopus, a mollusc.

7. Which are vertebrates and to what class does each belong?

   The vertebrates are the chicken, a bird (Aves), and the human, a mammal.

8. Based on the preceding limited amino acid sequences, which animal has the hedgehog protein most like the one in the human?

   Chicken. The amino acid sequence is the same as the human's.

9. Which organism has the most differences in the amino acid sequence compared to the human hedgehog protein sequence?

   Octopus. The octopus has 11 differences from the human, the scorpion only 9.

10. Would you have predicted the answers to questions 8 and 9? Why or why not?

    We think most learners would be able to make this prediction. If the gene is homologous, one would expect to see increased differences over time. These organisms belong to distinct groups associated with geologic time periods. The octopus is a mollusc, the scorpion is an arthropod, the chicken a bird, and the human a mammal.

III. Critical Reading: Stem Cells and Gene Expression

Chapters 18 and 20 explore the basic question of how cells with the same DNA can become different cell types. Cell biologists cite differential gene expression in cells as the explanation. They are working with stem cells to better understand the regulation of gene expression in both developing and adult organisms. Cell signaling pathways play a critical role in this gene regulation, but it is important to note that pathways such as the hedgehog pathway have different roles in embryonic and adult stem cells.

With the exception of gametes, a complete set of chromosomes is found in all cells in the human body. However, not all genes are expressed in each cell. The proteins necessary for cell function depend on the location and function of a particular cell in the body as well as the specific conditions the cell confronts during its survival in the body.

1. Specify the location of a cell in your body that:

   a. contains genetic information on eye color and the production of insulin.

   Open—cells anywhere in the body

   b. expresses eye color.

   Cell in the iris of the eye

   c. produces insulin.

   Beta cells of the pancreas

Over the last century, cell determination in the developing embryo has been closely observed. New methods and tools enable modern scientists to probe this process at the molecular level.

2. What is the molecular definition of *determination*?

   Expression of tissue-specific proteins

3. What molecules provide the earliest evidence that a cell is committed to a particular cell fate?

   mRNAs

   Stem cells are distinct from most cells in animals because they retain the ability to divide and remain relatively undifferentiated. Under certain conditions, however, stem cells divide and a subset of the new cells differentiates into specific cell types.

4. What are the major differences between stem cells found in embryonic tissue and those found in adult tissues?

   Embryonic or fetal stem cells are totipotent, i.e., are believed to be able to give rise to all kinds of cells. Adult stem cells are pluripotent, that is, are restricted to the kinds of cells they can become.

   Embryonic stem cells derive from the blastula and give rise to all the differentiated cells necessary to the development of the fetus. In humans, embryonic stem cells begin to disappear within 2 years after birth.

   Adult stem cells function primarily to maintain and repair specific tissues and are continuing to be discovered in new locations within the adult body.

The current interest in stem cells for regulation of gene expression is tied to providing potential new therapies for treatment of diseases such as the use of hedgehog pathway antagonists.

Current research with adult stem cells has provided some unexpected results (Figure 10.5).

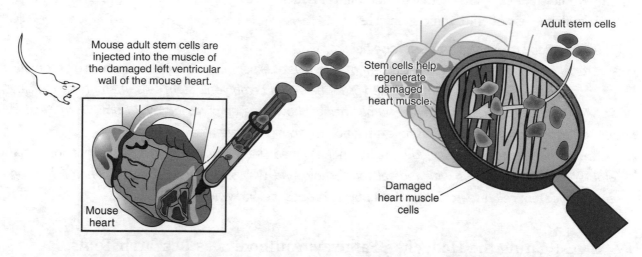

Figure 10.5 Mouse bone marrow stem cells injected into a damaged mouse heart resulted in new heart tissue. The bone marrow stem cells appear to secrete factors that promote regeneration.

Reference for image:
Stem Cell Basics: What are the potential uses of human stem cells and the obstacles that must be overcome before these potential uses will be realized? 2006. In *Stem Cell Information* (World Wide Web site). Bethesda, MD: National Institutes of Health, U.S. Department of Health and Human Services (cited Tuesday, June 19, 2007). Available at http://stemcells.nih.gov/info/basics/basics6.

5. To what kinds of cells can adult bone marrow cells give rise?

   Bone, cartilage, fat, muscle, nervous tissue, blood, and the linings of blood vessels.

6. Describe why human adult stem cells from bone marrow are used to treat patients who have undergone radiation treatments.

   Stem cells are used as a source of immune system cells in patients whose own immune systems have become nonfunctional due to radiation.

7. Provide an example of how treatment with cultured embryonic stem cells could be used to supply cells for the repair of damaged or diseased organs in human patients.

   • *Insulin-producing pancreatic cells for patients with diabetes*

   • *Kinds of brain cells for patients with Parkinson's disease or Huntington's disease*

8. Use of adult stem cells is well accepted; however, these cells have limited use as donor cells. Human embryonic stem cells have greater potential uses in a wider variety of tissues; however, the use of embryonic stem cells raises ethical and political issues. Identify two concerns an individual might have with the use of embryonic stem cells.

There are many issues students can raise here:

Ethical questions relate to: development of and trials of experimental treatments; the use of somatic cell nuclear transfer (SCNT) to make embryos for harvesting embryonic stem cells; if embryos made by SCNT should be considered separate human beings; how extra embryos left over from IVF are treated and/or discarded; the ethics of using extra embryos from IVF as stem cell sources.

The political issues might include: the ban in the United States regarding establishment of additional embryonic stem cell lines with federal funds; how and why states are permitting and/or funding embryonic stem cell research; who the lobbying groups are and why.

IV. Investigating the Hedgehog Pathway: Antibodies as Research Tools

Scientists ingeniously design research tools based on *in vivo* processes of biological systems. For example, PCR is a technique utilizing the enzyme DNA polymerase to initiate the synthesis of a minuscule DNA sample. Likewise, Western blots and immunohistochemistry are techniques utilizing the highly specific binding of antibodies with target molecules to act as molecular probes in cells and tissues.

1. Explain how an antibody is able to recognize a specific antigen. (Include an explanation of an epitope in your answer.)

There is a molecular interaction between the antibody and the antigen. A very small portion of the antigen molecule, called the epitope or antigenic determinant, is recognized by the antibody.

Antibody Techniques

Antibodies can be used to find, bind, and tag a specific molecule of interest. Antibodies are Y-shaped molecules, with the tips of the Y containing unique amino acid sequences that bind the antigen. These variable portions of antibody molecules convey the high specificity for a target molecule. The large tail or base of the Y is much less variable. In fact, all antibodies within a species have tail regions that are very similar in sequence and shape. By inserting compounds that fluoresce, produce radiation, or produce a color change in the tail region of these molecules, researchers can use antibodies as marker molecules.

Often, researchers use two different antibodies: a primary antibody for targeting the molecule of interest and a secondary antibody with active sites to bind the primary antibody's tail and act as a marker.

Western blots are used to detect the presence of a known protein in a given sample. The proteins are first separated by molecular weight using gel electrophoresis. Next, the proteins are transferred from the gel to a nitrocellose membrane in a process called blotting. The nitrocellulose membrane is then incubated with a primary antibody that combines with the protein of interest. Then an enzyme coupled with a secondary antibody is used to produce a detectable color change when the protein of interest is present. The intensity of the color change indicates the quantity of the protein.

Immunohistochemistry uses antibodies to detect the presence of specific molecules, usually proteins, within tissues and cells. Thin sections of a biological sample are fixed to a glass slide, incubated with primary and secondary antibodies, and examined microscopically. Secondary antibodies used in immuno-histochemistry are frequently fluorescent, in which case a fluorescent microscope is used to read the results.

2. Briefly describe what you can learn about a target protein by using each of these two techniques.

Western blots allow you to detect whether a specific protein is present in a sample.
Immunohistochemistry allows you to see where in the organism or cell the protein is present.

In 1996, it was discovered that a mutation in the *Patched* gene in the hedgehog pathway was involved in almost all cases of basal cell nevus syndrome, a rare hereditary syndrome of birth defects and multiple BCC starting early in life. This autosomal recessive mutation was identified in families affected by the syndrome. The *Patched* mutation resulted in a nonfunctional Patched protein.

3. Refer to the hedgehog pathway diagram (Figure 10.4) and explain what happens when the Patched protein is nonfunctional.

Normally, Patched inhibits Smoothened. Without a functional Patched protein, the Smoothened protein continuously initiates Gli transcription. The Patched protein is also the receptor for the hedgehog sig-naling protein. When hedgehog protein attaches to Patched, Smoothened is released from inhibition.

4. How could this lead to cancer?

The basal cells are uncontrolled. Abnormal transcription and cell division result.

As soon as the hedgehog pathway was implicated, researchers began looking at inhibitors that might serve as chemotherapy for this common cancer. Cyclopamine, the plant teratogen known to interfere with the hedgehog signaling pathway in early development, showed potential as a cancer treatment.

The exact mechanism by which cyclopamine inhibits hedgehog pathway signaling has been a topic of controversy. One hypothesis was that cyclopamine prevented the secretion of Shh from Shh-pro-ducing cells. The protein was expressed but without its normal cholesterol addition. As a result, Shh could not leave the cell to act as a signaling protein.

5. If you were asked to test this hypothesis, which technique do you think would be more useful—Western blots or immunohistochemistry? Explain your choice.

The immunohistochemistry technique is a good way to detect Shh inside and outside of cells, not just confirm its presence.

The following experiment was designed to test the effect of cyclopamine on Shh secretion:

Chick embryos in embryonic Day 3 (cells known to secrete Shh) are divided into cyclopamine-treated groups and control groups. After an established exposure time, embryos from both groups are sacrificed and then sectioned for immunohistochemistry testing. Samples are incubated with pri-mary, then secondary, antibodies per an established protocol. Under fluorescent microscopy, tissues are assessed for the presence and location of Shh.

Table 10.1 Antibodies for Hedgehog Proteins.

Order Number	Protein	Tissue Specificity	Antibody Type and Source
1223	Hh	Drosophila	*Anti-Hh* goat, polyclonal
1224	Hh	Drosophila	*Anti-Hh* rabbit, polyclonal
2011	Ptc	Drosophila	*Anti-Ptc* goat, polyclonal
2624	Ptch	Mouse, rat, human, chicken	*Anti-Ptch* rabbit, polyclonal
2680	Ptch	Mouse, rat, human	*Anti-Ptch* goat, polyclonal
2681	Ptch	Mouse, rat, human	*Anti-Ptch* goat, polyclonal
2626	Ptch	Mouse, rat, human, chicken	*Anti-Ptch* rabbit, polyclonal
4235	Shh	Mouse, human	*Anti-Shh* mouse, monoclonal
4257	Shh	Human	*Anti-Shh* rabbit, polyclonal
4278	Shh	Mouse, human	*Anti-Shh* rat, monoclonal
4279	Shh	Mouse	*Anti-Shh* goat, polyclonal
4284	Shh	Mouse, rat, human, primate, chicken, cat	*Anti-Shh* goat, polyclonal
4286	Shh	Mouse, rat, human, zebrafish, Xenopus	*Anti-Shh* rabbit, polyclonal
3511	Smo	Drosophila	*Anti-Smo* mouse, monoclonal
6766	Smo	Mouse, rat, human	*Anti-Smo* rabbit, polyclonal
6788	Smo	Mouse, rat, human	*Anti-Smo* goat, polyclonal
6789	Smo	Drosophila	*Anti-Smo* goat, polyclonal

Based on a page from a research supply company catalog.

6. Consider the antibodies for hedgehog proteins listed in Table 10.1. Which one of these primary antibodies would you choose for the experiment described earlier? Why?

The primary antibody #4284, Goat anti-Shh, polyclonal. This is the only one that binds with the chicken Shh epitope.

7. The secondary antibody includes a fluorescent marker in its tail region. Why?

To show where the Shh protein is located.

The results of this experiment showed no difference between the test and the control specimens in the amount of fluorescence inside and outside the cells.

8. What can you conclude from these results?

In this experiment, cyclopamine does not appear to inhibit Shh secretion.

New evidence suggests that cyclopamine's effect on the pathway may be caused by inhibiting Smoothened. Therefore, even in the presence of Shh, no message is transduced to the nucleus by Gli and, therefore, there is no cellular response.

9. Consider the use of cyclopamine as a chemotherapeutic agent in cases of spontaneous BCC. Researchers discovered that this cancer results from a mutation of *Patched*. If cyclopamine was approved for human use, would you recommend it for these cases of BCC? Why or why not?

Yes. Patched mutants lose their inhibitory effect on Smoothened and the pathway is inappropriately activated. Cyclopamine seemingly restores inhibition on Smoothened.

Suggested Answers for Additional Investigations

V. Open-Ended Investigations

To learn more about the hedgehog pathway, you could explore the Hedgehog Pathway Signaling Database (Ramirez-Weber, 2006), which contains relevant information, images, and references to research articles. You may wish to form a group to develop a proposal for a new investigation. For example:

- Explore a known hedgehog pathway antagonist other than cyclopamine.
  - How does this antagonist disrupt the pathway?
  - Does the antagonist have potential as a chemotherapeutic drug?
  - What organism produces this antagonist molecule and how is it useful in that organism?
- Choose one of the molecules in the pathway and compare the genes using Biology Workbench.

Note: Your instructor could set up a proposal peer review process in your class, simulating what is done by major funders such as the National Science Foundation and the National Institutes of Health.

References

Anonymous. 2006. Stem Cell Basics: What are the potential uses of human stem cells and the obstacles that must be overcome before these potential uses will be realized? In *Stem Cell Information* [World Wide Web site]. Bethesda, MD: National Institutes of Health, U.S. Department of Health and Human Services, 2006. http://stemcells.nih.gov/info/basics/basics6 (accessed June 19, 2007).

Athar, Mohammad, Chengxin Li , Xiuwei Tang, Sumin Chi, Xiaoli Zhang, Arianna L. Kim, Stephen K. Tyring, Levy Kopelovich, Jennifer Hebert, Ervin H. Epstein Jr., David R. Bickers, and Jingwu Xie. 15 October 2004. Inhibition of smoothened signaling prevents ultraviolet B-induced basal cell carcinomas through regulation of Fas expression and apoptosis. Cancer Research 64:7545–7552, 2004. http://cancerres.aacrjournals.org/cgi/content/full/64/20/7545#F2 (accessed September 2007).

Cancerquest. http://www.cancerquest.org (accessed September 2007).

Chen, James K., Jussi Taipale, Michael K. Cooper, and Philip A. Beachy. 2002. Inhibition of hedgehog signaling by direct binding of cyclopamine to Smoothened. Genes and Development 16:2743–2748, 2002. http://www.genesdev.org/cgi/content/full/16/21/2743 (accessed September 2007).

Johnson, R. L., A. L. Rothman, J. Xie, L. V. Goodrich, J. W. Bare, J. M. Bonifas, A. G. Quinn, R. M. Myers, D. R. Cox, E. H. Epstein Jr., and M. P. Scott. 1996. Human homolog of Patched, a candidate gene for the basal cell nevus syndrome. *Science* 272:1668–1671, 1996.

Kumar, S., K. Balczarek, and Z. Lai. 1996. Evolution of the hedgehog gene family. *Genetics* 142:965–972, 1996.

Matlack, David. June 2007. Private communication regarding the use of immunohistochemistry and antibodies, June 2007.

Matlack, D., P. Pape-Lindstrom, and S. Webb. 2006. Hedgehog-emony: BioQUEST Complex Data Sets Workshop Project. http://bioquest.org/summer2006/workshop_forms/project_template.php?project_id=251 (accessed June 21, 2007).

Ramirez-Weber, F. A. 2006. The Hedgehog Signaling Pathway Database. NIH RIMI 5P20-MD000262. San Francisco State University. http://hedgehog.sfsu.edu/ (accessed July 3, 2007).

Weitzman, J. G. 2002. Agonizing hedgehog. *Journal of Biology* 2002 1:7. Online at http://jbiol.com/content/1/2/7 (accessed September 2007).